easy Guitar

All-Time Hits

Wise Publications
don/New York/Paris/Sydney/Copenhagen/Madrid/Tokyo

C000046295

Exclusive Distributers
Music Sales Limited
8-9 Frith Street,
London W1V 5TZ, England.
Music Sales Pty Limited
120 Rothschild Avenue,
Rosebery, NSW 2018,
Australia.

Order No. AM951951
ISBN 0-7119-7945-6
This book © Copyright 1999 by Wise Publications

Compiled by Peter Evans
Music arranged by Rob Smith
Music processed by Andrew Shiels
Cover design by Studio Twenty, London
Cover photography by Julian Hawkins
Printed in the United Kingdom by Redwood Books, Trowbridge.

Your Guarantee of Quality
As publishers, we strive to produce every book to
the highest commercial standards.
The music has been freshly engraved and the book
has been carefully designed to minimise awkward
page turns and to make playing from it a real
pleasure.
Particular care has been given to specifying acid-
free, neutral-sized paper made from pulps which
have not been elemental chlorine bleached. This
pulp is from farmed sustainable forests and was
produced with special regard for the environment.
Throughout, the printing and binding have been
planned to ensure a sturdy, attractive publication
which should give years of enjoyment.
If your copy fails to meet our high standards, please
inform us and we will gladly replace it.

Music Sales' complete catalogue describes
thousands of titles and is available in full colour
sections by subject, direct from Music Sales
Limited. Please state your areas of interest and
send a cheque/postal order for £1.50 for postage
to: Music Sales Limited, Newmarket Road, Bury St.
Edmunds, Suffolk IP33 3YB.

www.musicsales.co.uk

Other titles in the
Easy Guitar series...
Chart Toppers
Order No. AM951930

Classic Hits
Order No. AM951940

Top Pops
Order No. AM951962

Three More easy *Guitar* Books
With 170 hits for you to play...

Featuring all these titles...

Addicted To Love *Robert Palmer*
Albatross *Fleetwood Mac*
All Shook Up *Elvis Presley*
All That She Wants *Ace Of Base*
American Pie *Don McLean*
Behind The Mask *Eric Clapton*
Bridge Over Troubled Water *Simon & Garfunkel*
Brothers In Arms *Dire Straits*
California Dreaming *The Mamas & The Papas*
Candle In The Wind *Elton John*
C'mon Everybody *Eddie Cochran*
Country House *Blur*
Crocodile Rock *Elton John*
Da Ya Think I'm Sexy? *Rod Stewart*
Disco 2000 *Pulp*
Easy Lover *Phil Bailey & Phil Collins*
Every Little Thing She Does Is Magic *The Police*
Exodus *Bob Marley*
15 Years *The Levellers*
Fifty Ways To Leave Your Lover *Paul Simon*
Get It On (Bang A Gong) *T. Rex*
Gimme All Your Lovin' *ZZ Top*
Have I Told You Lately? *Van Morrison*
Hey Jude *The Beatles*
I Will *The Beatles*
If I Ever Lose My Faith In You *Sting*
Imagine *John Lennon*
In The City *Jam*
Instant Karma *John Lennon*
Just Can't Get Enough *Depeche Mode*
Keep The Faith *Bon Jovi*
Linger *The Cranberries*
Me And Julio Down By The Schoolyard *Paul Simon*
Missing *Everything But The Girl*
Mrs Robinson *Simon & Garfunkel*
My Father's Eyes *Eric Clapton*
Oh Boy *Buddy Holly*
Peggy Sue *Buddy Holly*
Pride (In The Name Of love) *U2*
Romeo And Juliet *Dire Straits*
Roxanne *The Police*
She Loves You *The Beatles*
So Lonely *The Police*
Spice Up Your Life *Spice Girls*
Sultans Of Swing *Dire Straits*
Summertime Blues *Eddie Cochran*
Sweet Dreams Are Made Of This *Eurythmics*
Take On Me *A-ha*
Thriller *Michael Jackson*
Vienna *Ultravox*
Vincent *Don McLean*
Walk Of Life *Dire Straits*
What's Love Got To Do With It *Tina Turner*
Wild Wood *Paul Weller*
Without You *Mariah Carey, Nilsson*
You Do Something To Me *Paul Weller*
You Give Love A Bad Name *Bon Jovi*

easy *Guitar*
Chart Toppers
Wise Publications
Order No. AM951930
ISBN 0-7119-7280-X

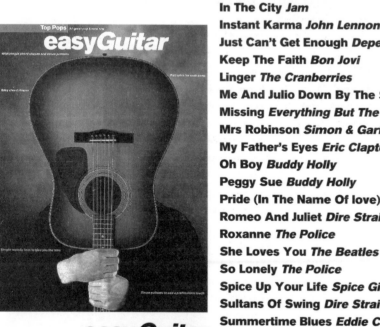

easy *Guitar*
Top Pops
Wise Publications
Order No. AM951962
ISBN 0-7119-7281-8

**Available from all
good music retailers
or, in case of difficulty,
direct from
Music Sales Limited,
Newmarket Road,
Bury St. Edmonds,
Suffolk IP33 3YB
Telephone 01284 725725
Fax 01284 702592**

Featuring all these titles...

After The Goldrush *Neil Young*
All Right Now *Free*
All You Need Is Love *The Beatles*
America *Simon & Garfunkel*
Barbie Girl *Aqua*
Big Yellow Taxi *Joni Mitchell*
Blue Suede Shoes *Elvis Presley*
Call Me *Blondie*
Careless Whisper *George Michael*
Cecilia *Simon & Garfunkel*
Common People *Pulp*
D'You Know What I Mean? *Oasis*
Dancing Queen *Abba*
Daniel *Elton John*
Don't You (Forget About Me) *Simple Minds*
Ebony and Ivory *Paul McCartney with Stevie Wonder*
Eight Days A Week *The Beatles*
Every Breath You Take *Police*
Everybody (Backstreet's Back) *Backstreet Boys*
Everyday *Buddy Holly*
(Everything I Do) I Do It For You *Bryan Adams*
Girls And Boys *Blur*
Good Vibrations *The Beach Boys*
Hanging On The Telephone *Blondie*
Heartbeat *Buddy Holly*
Hotel California *Eagles*
I Shall Be Released *Bob Dylan*
I Shot The Sheriff *Bob Marley*
In The Air Tonight *Phil Collins*
Ironic *Alanis Morissette*
Jamming *Bob Marley*
Jealous Guy *John Lennon*
Just Like A Woman *Bob Dylan*
Lyin' Eyes *Eagles*
Money For Nothing *Dire Straits*
No More Heroes *Stranglers*
Norwegian Wood *The Beatles*
One More Night *Phil Collins*
Paperback Writer *The Beatles*
Pinball Wizard *The Who*
Private Investigations *Dire Straits*
Proud Mary *Creedence Clearwater Revival*
Remember How We Started *Paul Weller*
Sailing *Rod Stewart*
Saturday Night *Suede*
She Bangs The Drums *The Stone Roses*
Stayin' Alive *The Bee Gees*
Still Crazy After All These Years *Paul Simon*
Tears In Heaven *Eric Clapton*
The Day We Caught The Train *Ocean Colour Scene*
The Riverboat Song *Ocean Colour Scene*
Tupelo Honey *Van Morrison*
Walking On The Moon *Police*
Waterloo Sunset *Kinks*
Where The Streets Have No Name *U2*
Wonderwall *Oasis*
Words *Boyzone/The Bee Gees*
Yesterday *The Beatles*
You Oughta Know *Alanis Morissette*
Your Song *Elton John*
Zombie *Cranberries*

Wise Publications
Order No. AM951940
ISBN 0-7119-7286-9

easy Guitar
Classic Hits

Featuring all these titles...

A Different Beat *Boyzone*
A Hard Rain's A Gonna Fall *Bob Dylan*
All Along The Watchtower *Bob Dylan*
Band On The Run *Wings*
Champagne Supernova *Oasis*
Eight Miles High *The Byrds*
Eternal Flame *The Bangles*
Fire And Water *Free*
Gloria *Van Morrison*
Going Underground *The Jam*
Goodnight Girl *Wet Wet Wet*
Hurdy Gurdy Man *Donovan*
I Still Haven't Found What I'm Looking For *U2*
I've Gotta Get A Message To You *The Bee Gees*
Jailhouse Rock *Elvis Presley*
Killing Me Softly With His Song *The Fugees*
Lay Down Sally *Eric Clapton*
Layla *Eric Clapton*
Like A Rolling Stone *Bob Dylan*
Lola *The Kinks*
Love Is All Around *Wet Wet Wet*
Love Me Do *The Beatles*
Love Me Tender *Elvis Presley*
Love The One You're With *Stephen Stills*
Mind Games *John Lennon*
No More "I Love You's" *Annie Lennox*
Ode To My Family *The Cranberries*
Picture Of You *Boyzone*
Pipes Of Peace *Paul McCartney*
Rave On *Buddy Holly*
Rebel Rebel *David Bowie*
Ridiculous Thoughts *The Cranberries*
She's A Star *James*
Sorted For E's And Wizz *Pulp*
Strange Town *The Jam*
Sunny Afternoon *The Kinks*
Super Trouper *Abba*
Supersonic *Oasis*
Take A Chance On Me *Abba*
Take My Breath Away *Berlin*
Telegram Sam *T. Rex*
That'll Be The Day *Buddy Holly*
The Changingman *Paul Weller*
The Jean Genie *David Bowie*
This Is Hardcore *Pulp*
Ticket To Ride *The Beatles*
Turn, Turn, Turn *The Byrds*
20th Century Boy *T. Rex*
Viva Forever *Spice Girls*
Words Of Love *Buddy Holly*
Yellow Submarine *The Beatles*
You Learn *Alanis Morissette*

A Hard Day's Night

Words & Music by John Lennon & Paul McCartney

When I'm home___ feel-ing you hold-ing me tight, tight, yeah.__ 3. It's been a

Verse

hard day's night___ and I've been work-ing like a dog.___ It's been a

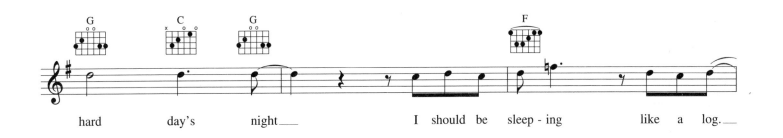

hard day's night___ I should be sleep-ing like a log.___

_____ But when I get home to you,___ I find the thing that you do___ will make me

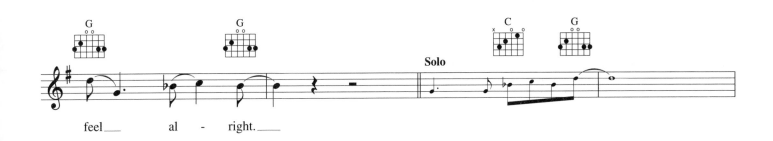

Solo

feel___ al-right.___

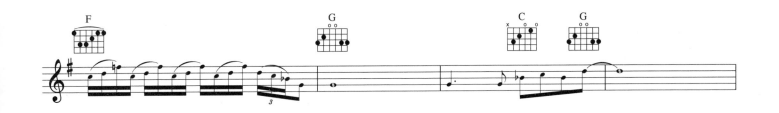

So why on earth should I moan_ 'Cause when I

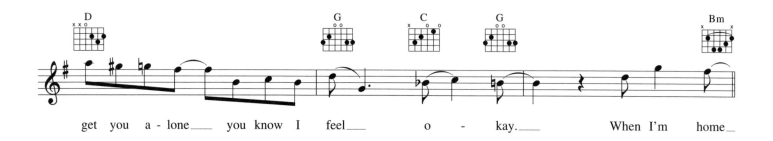

get you a - lone___ you know I feel__ o - kay.___ When I'm home__

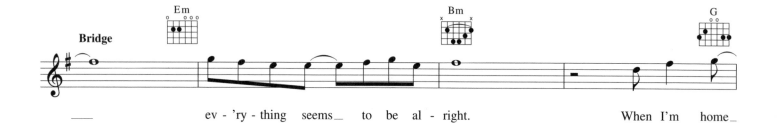

Bridge

__ ev - 'ry - thing seems_ to be al - right. When I'm home__

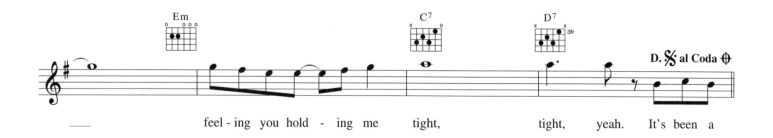

D. 𝄋 al Coda ⊕

__ feel - ing you hold - ing me tight, tight, yeah. It's been a

⊕ Coda

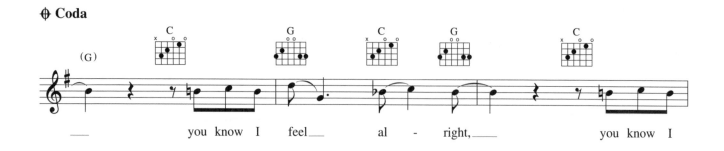

(G)

__ you know I feel__ al - right,___ you know I

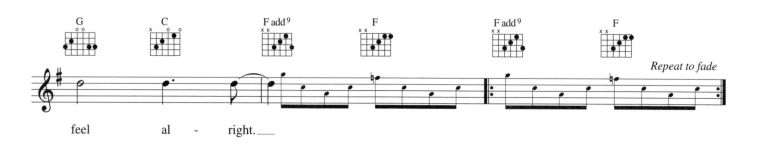

Repeat to fade

feel al - right.___

Always

Words & Music by Jon Bon Jovi

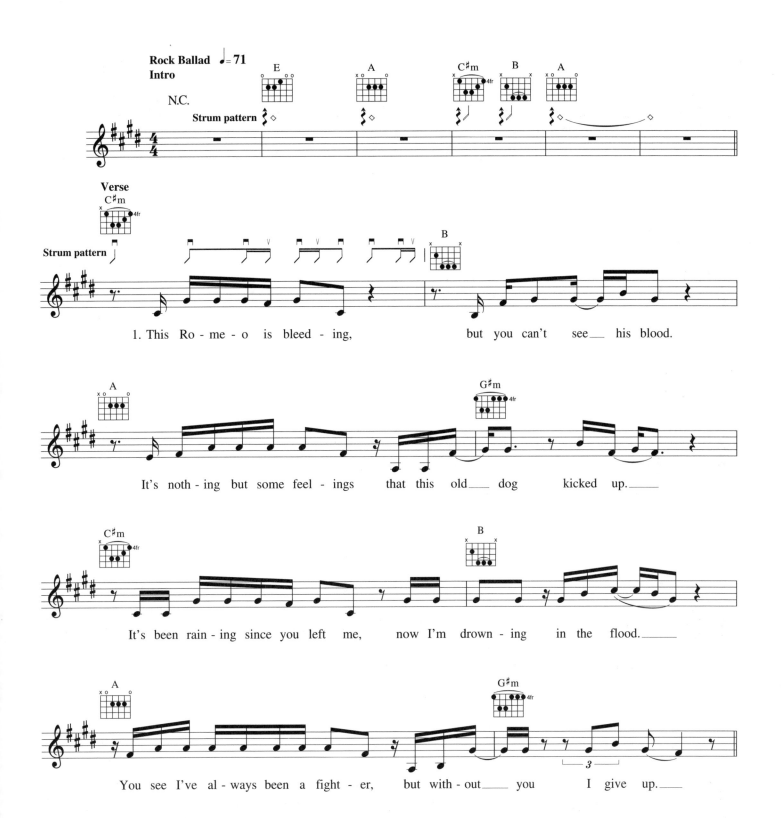

1. This Ro-me-o is bleed-ing, but you can't see__ his blood.

It's noth-ing but some feel-ings that this old__ dog kicked up.__

It's been rain-ing since you left me, now I'm drown-ing in the flood.__

You see I've al-ways been a fight-er, but with-out__ you I give up.__

Pre-chorus

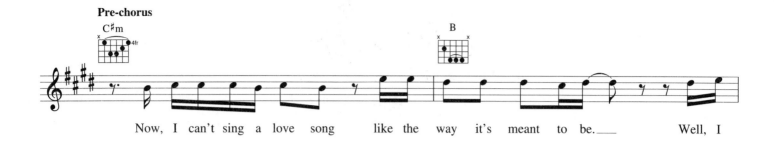

Now, I can't sing a love song like the way it's meant to be.___ Well, I

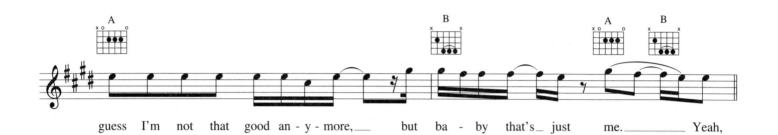

guess I'm not that good an - y - more,___ but ba - by that's_ just me._____ Yeah,

Chorus

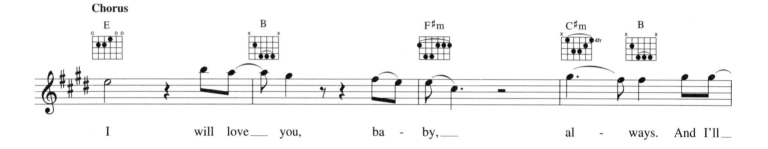

I will love___ you, ba - by,___ al - ways. And I'll_

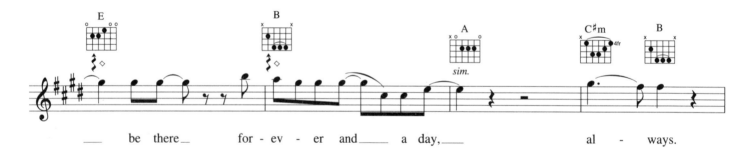

___ be there___ for - ev - er and___ a day,___ al - ways.

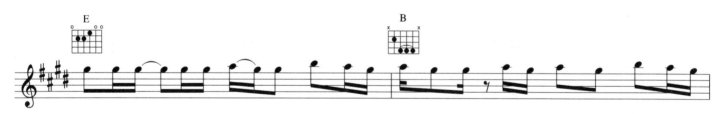

I'll be there___ till the stars_ don't shine, till the heav - ens burst and the words don't rhyme. I know

when I die___ you'll be on my mind, and I love___ you, al - ways.___

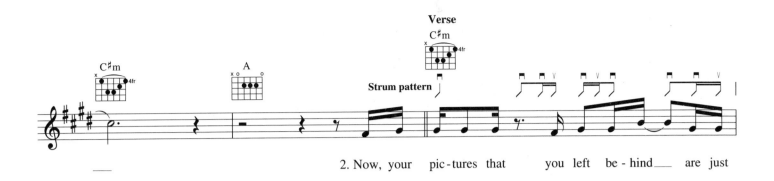

Verse

Strum pattern

2. Now, your pic-tures that you left be-hind___ are just

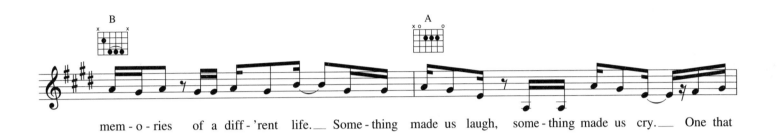

mem - o - ries of a diff - 'rent life.___ Some-thing made us laugh, some-thing made us cry.___ One that

made_ you have to say good-bye.___ What I'd give to run my fin-gers through your hair,___

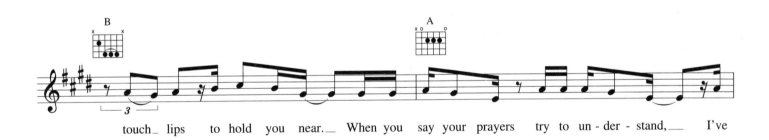

touch_ lips to hold you near.___ When you say your prayers try to un - der - stand,___ I've

Pre-chorus

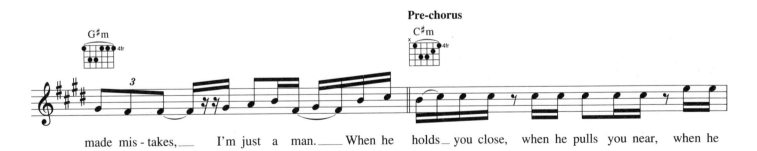

made mis-takes,___ I'm just a man.___ When he holds_ you close, when he pulls you near, when he

says the words___ you've been mean-ing to hear. I wish I was him with those words of mine,_ just to

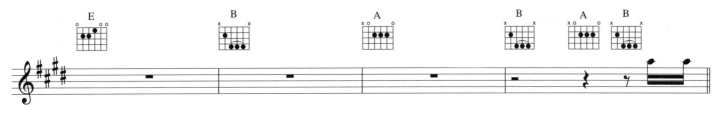

Well, there

Bridge

Strum pattern

ain't no luck   in these load - ed dice.___ But ba - by, if you give me just one more try,___ we could

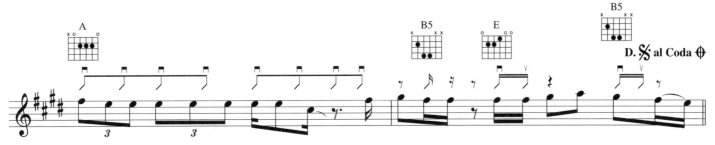

D. 𝄋 al Coda ⊕

pack up our old dreams and our old lives.   We'll find a place   where the sun still shines. Yeah,___

⊕ **Coda**

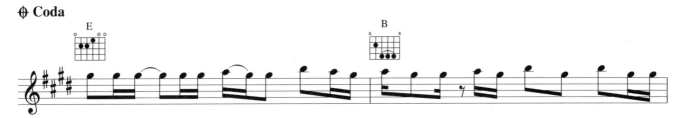

I'll be there_ till the stars_don't shine, til the heav - ens burst and the words don't rhyme. I know

when I die___ you'll be on___ my mind,___ and I love___ you,   al - ways._____

Outro

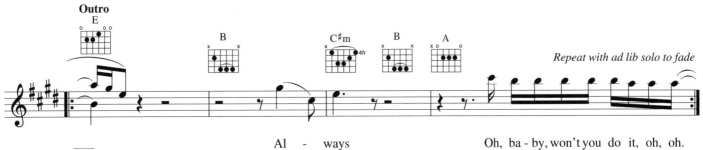

Repeat with ad lib solo to fade

___   Al - ways   Oh, ba - by, won't you do it, oh, oh.

13

All Day And All Of The Night

Words & Music by Ray Davies

Blowin' In The Wind

Words & Music by Bob Dylan

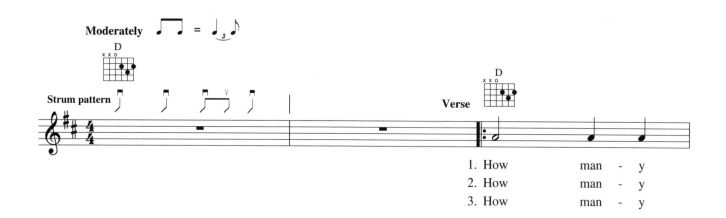

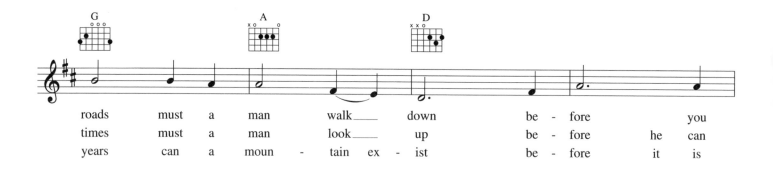

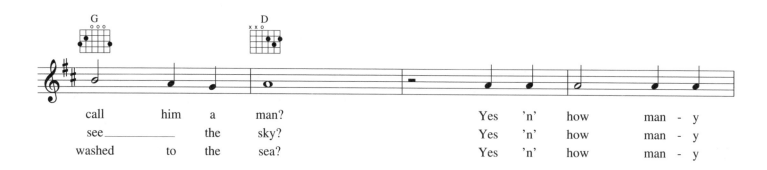

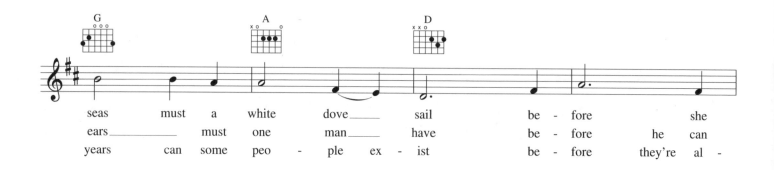

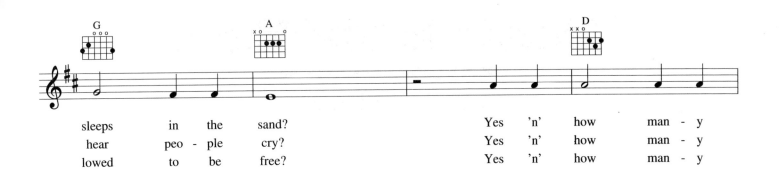

sleeps   in   the   sand?   Yes   'n'   how   man - y
hear   peo - ple   cry?   Yes   'n'   how   man - y
lowed   to   be   free?   Yes   'n'   how   man - y

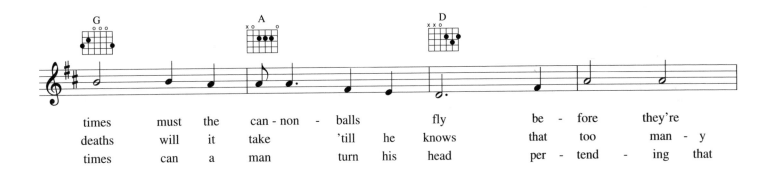

times   must   the   can - non - balls   fly   be - fore   they're
deaths   will   it   take   'till   he   knows   that   too   man - y
times   can   a   man   turn   his   head   per - tend - ing   that

Chorus

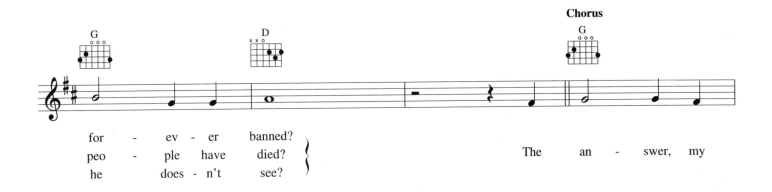

for - ev - er   banned?   The   an - swer,   my
peo - ple   have   died?
he   does - n't   see?

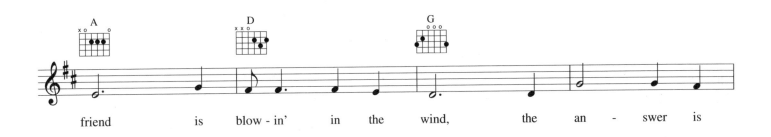

friend   is   blow - in'   in   the   wind,   the   an - swer   is

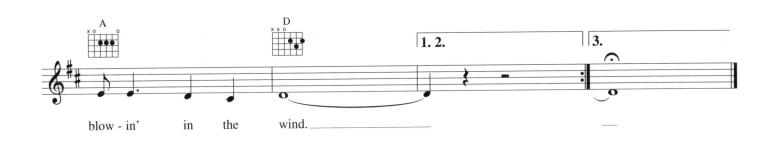

blow - in'   in   the   wind.

Born To Be Wild

Words & Music by Mars Bonfire

1.(%) Get your mo - tor run - ning,_____
2. I like smoke and light - nin',_____

head out on the high - way,
hea - vy met - al thun - der,

look - in' for ad - ven - ture
rac - in' with the wind_____

and what - ev - er comes our____ way.____
and the feel - in' that I'm un - der.____

Yeah, dar - lin' go make it hap - pen,

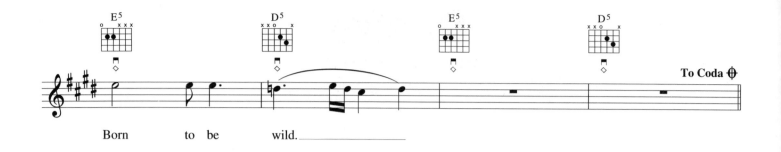

Born   to   be   wild._____

Organ solo

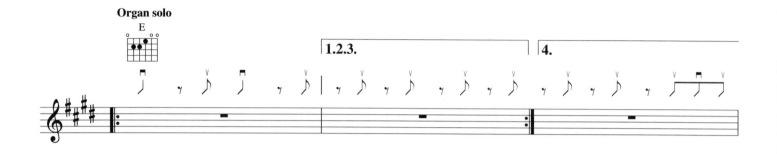

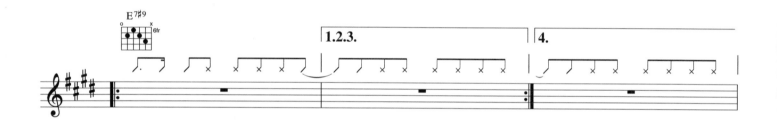

⊕ **Coda**

Repeat ad lib to fade

Desire

Words & Music by U2

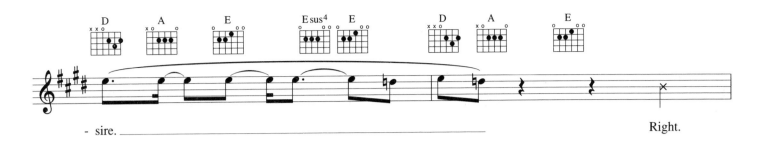

- sire. _____ Right.

And the

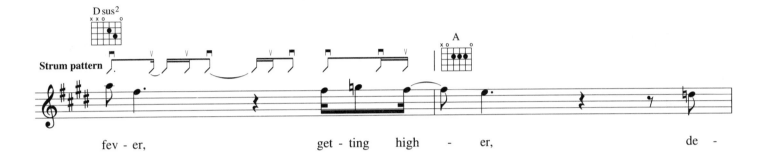

fev - er,   get - ting high - er,   de -

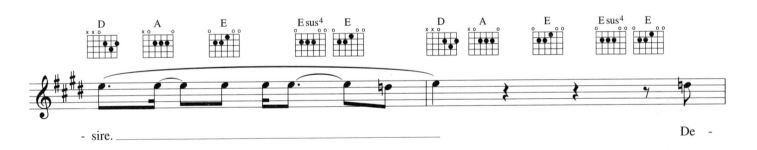

- sire. _____ De -

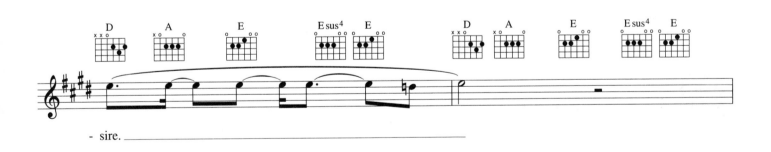

- sire. _____

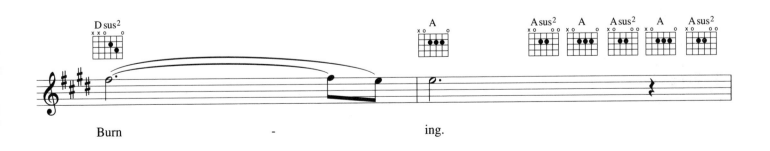

Burn -   ing.

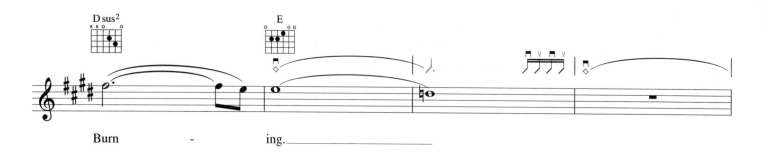

Burn - ing._____

Verse

She's the dol - lars, she's my pro - tec-

- tion. Yeah she's a prom - ise,_____ in the year of el - ec-

- tion. Oh sis - ter,_____ I can't let_____ you go._____ Like a

preach - er steal - ing hearts_____ at a tra - vel - ling_____ show. For love or

mo - ney, mo - ney, mo - ney, mo - ney, mo - ney, mo - ney, mo - ney, mo - ney, mo - ney, mo - ney, mo - ney and the

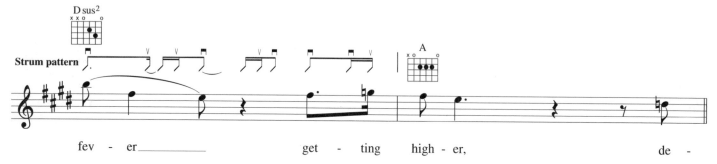

fev - er_____ get - ting high - er, de -

Father And Son

Words & Music by Cat Stevens

* Capo 1st fret

1. It's not

Verse

time to make__ a change;__ just re - lax,_____ take it ea - sy. You're still

(Verses 2 see block lyric)

young, that's your fault;__ there's so much you have__ to know.__ Find__ a girl,

__ set - tle down;__ if you want,_____ you__ can mar - ry. Look at me:

1.

__ I am old__ but I'm hap - py. 2. I was

Strum pattern

go. It's not time to make a change,___ just sit down___ ___ and take it slow - ly. You're still young, that's your fault;___ there's so much you have___ to go through. Find___ a girl,___ set - tle down;___ if you want,___ ___ you___ can mar - ry. Look at me___ I am old___ but I'm hap - py. 4. All the

D. 𝄋 al Coda ⊕

⊕ Coda

Strum pattern

have to go___ a - way.___ I know___ I have___ to go.

Verse 2:
I was once like you are now
And I know that it's not easy
To be calm when you've found something going on
But take your time, think a lot
Think of everything you've got
For you will still be here tomorrow.
But your dreams may not.

Verse 4:
All the times that I've cried
Keeping all the things I knew inside
And it's hard, but it's harder to ignore it
If they were right I'd agree
But it's them they know, not me
Now there's a way, and I know
That I have to go away
I know I have to go.

Free Bird

Words & Music by Allen Collins & Ronnie Van Zant

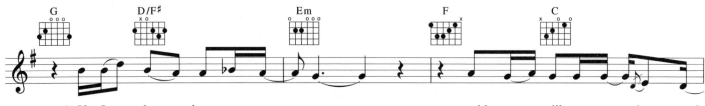

1. If I___ leave___ here to-mor-row,_____ would you___ still re-mem-ber___ me?___
2. Bye___bye, ba-by, it's been sweet___ now, yeah yeah. Though this feel - in' I___ can't change.___

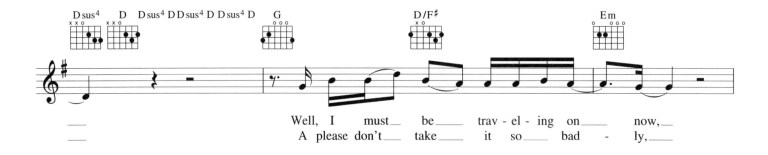

___ Well, I must___ be___ trav-el-ing on___ now,___
___ A please don't___ take___ it so___ bad-ly,___

'cause there's too man-y plac-es I've___ got to see.___
'cause the Lord knows I'm to blame.

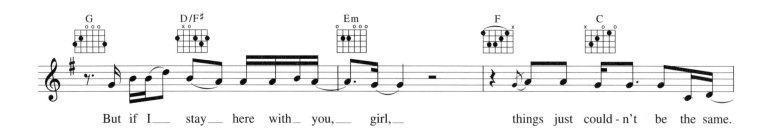

But if I___ stay___ here with___ you,___ girl,___ things just could-n't be the same.___

___ 'Cause I'm as___ free___ as a bird___ now,___

Get Back

Words & Music by John Lennon & Paul McCartney

33

Glad All Over

Words & Music by Dave Clark & Mike Smith

Intro ♩ = 141

N.C.

Strum pattern

1. You say that you

Verse

(Verse 3(%) see block lyric)

love me (say you love me) all of the time, (all of the time).
hap - py, (make you happy) you'll nev - er be blue, (never be blue).

You say that you need me (say you need me) you'll al - ways be
You'll have no sor - row, (no, no sorrow) 'cause I'll al - ways be

Chorus

mine, (always be mine). I'm feel - in' glad all ov -
true, (always be true). And I'm feel - in' glad all ov -

- er, yes I'm - a glad all ov - er. Ba - by I'm glad all ov -

Hand In My Pocket

Music by Alanis Morissette & Glenn Ballard
Words by Alanis Morissette

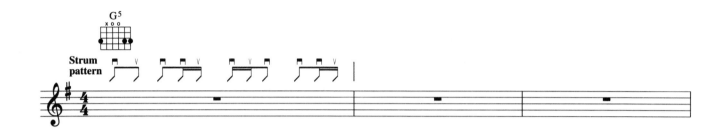

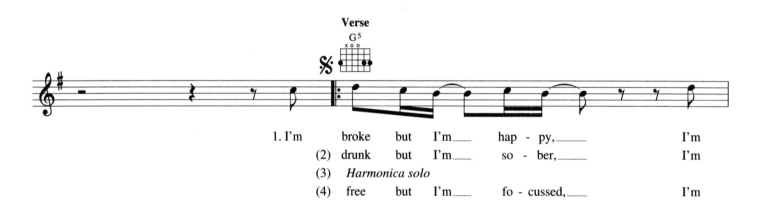

1. I'm broke but I'm____ hap - py,_____ I'm
(2) drunk but I'm____ so - ber,_____ I'm
(3) *Harmonica solo*
(4) free but I'm____ fo - cussed,_____ I'm

poor but I'm kind,_____ I'm short but I'm____ health - y, yeah._____
young and I'm under - paid, I'm tired but I'm____ work - ing, yeah._____
green but I'm wise,_____ I'm hard but I'm____ friend - ly ba -

____ I'm____ high but I'm ground - ed, I'm
____ I____ care but I'm rest - less, I'm
- by. I'm____ sad but I'm laugh - ing. I'm

sane　but　I'm　ov - er - whelmed,　　I'm　lost　but　I'm　hope - ful,　ba -
here　but　I'm　real - ly＿＿＿＿ gone,　　I'm　wrong　and　I'm　sor - ry　ba -
brave　but　I'm　chick - en＿＿＿ shit,　　I'm　sick　but　I'm　pret - ty　ba -

Chorus
G⁵/F

- by.
- by.　　And　what　it　all　comes　down＿＿＿ to
- by.

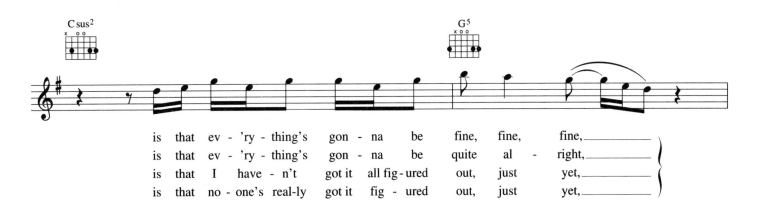

Csus²　　　　　　　　　　　　　　　　　　G⁵

is　that　ev - 'ry - thing's　gon - na　be　fine,　fine,　fine,＿＿＿＿＿＿
is　that　ev - 'ry - thing's　gon - na　be　quite　al - right,＿＿＿＿＿
is　that　I　have - n't　got it　all fig - ured　out,　just　yet,＿＿＿＿＿
is　that　no - one's　real - ly　got it　fig - ured　out,　just　yet,＿＿＿＿＿

G⁵/F

'cause　I've＿＿ got　a　one　hand　in　my　pock - et　　　and　the

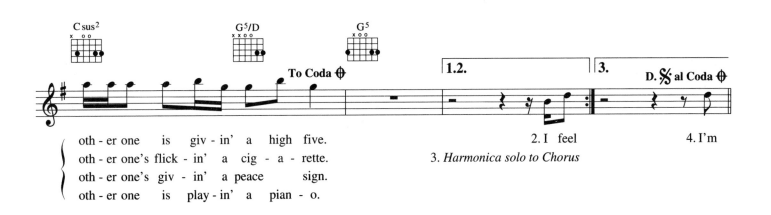

Csus²　　　　　　　G⁵/D　　　　　G⁵

To Coda ⊕　　　　**1.2.**　　　　　　　**3.**　　　**D. 𝄋 al Coda** ⊕

oth - er　one　is　giv - in' a　high　five.　　　　　　　2. I feel　　　　　4. I'm
oth - er　one's　flick - in' a　cig - a - rette.
oth - er　one's　giv - in' a　peace　sign.　　　　3. *Harmonica solo to Chorus*
oth - er　one　is　play - in' a　pian - o.

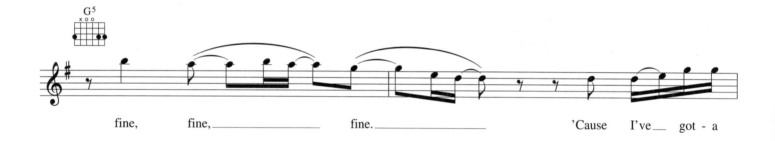

And what it all comes down

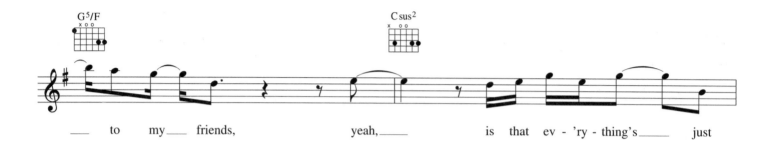

to my friends, yeah, is that ev - 'ry - thing's just

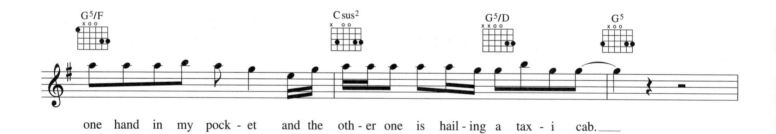

fine, fine, fine. 'Cause I've got - a

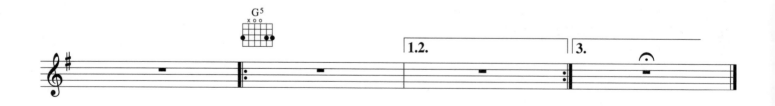

one hand in my pock - et and the oth - er one is hail - ing a tax - i cab.

His Latest Flame
(Marie's The Name)

Words & Music by Doc Pomus & Mort Shuman

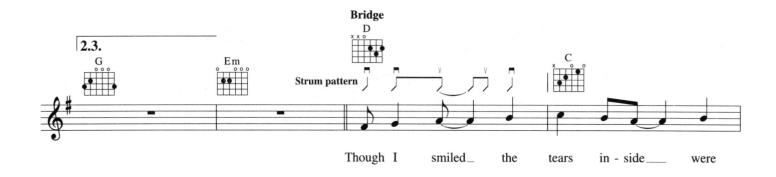

Though I smiled_ the tears in - side___ were

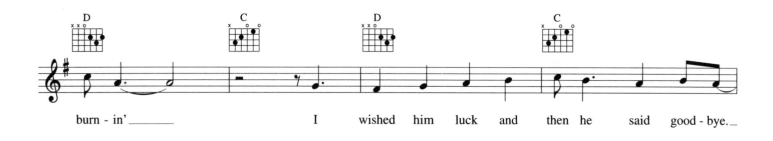

burn - in'_____ I wished him luck and then he said good - bye._

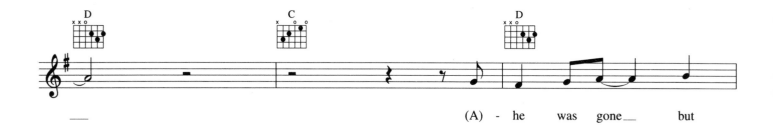

___ (A) - he was gone__ but

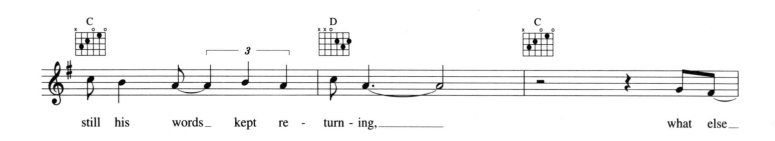

still his words_ kept re - turn - ing,_____ what else_

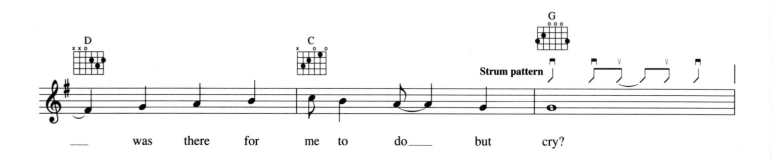

___ was there for me to do___ but cry?

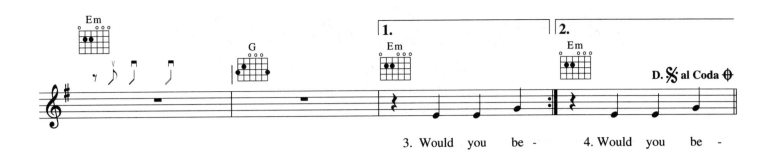

3. Would you be - 4. Would you be -

⊕ Coda

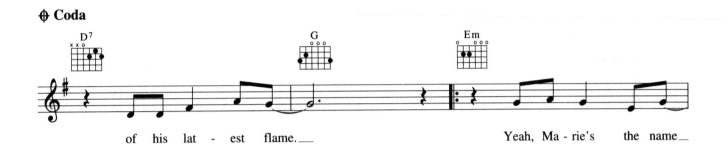

of his lat - est flame.___ Yeah, Ma - rie's the name___

Repeat to fade

___ of his lat - est flame.

Verse 2:   He talked and talked, and I heard him say
That she had the longest black hair
The prettiest green eyes anywhere
And Marie's the name of his latest flame.

Verse 3:   Would you believe that yesterday
This girl was in my arms and swore to me
She'd be mine eternally
And Marie's the name of his latest flame.

Verse 4(𝄋)   As *Verse 3*

Highway 61 Revisited

Words & Music by Bob Dylan

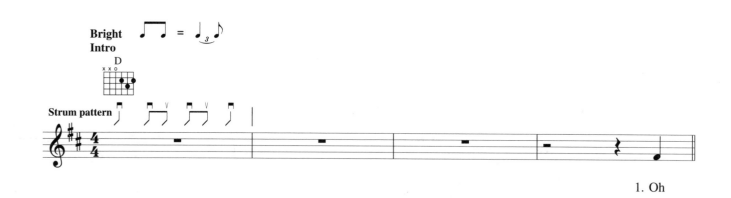

1. Oh

1. God said to A - bra - ham; kill me a son. Abe says man you must be

(Verses 2–5 see block lyric)

put - tin' me on.__ God say no, Abe say what? God say you can do what you

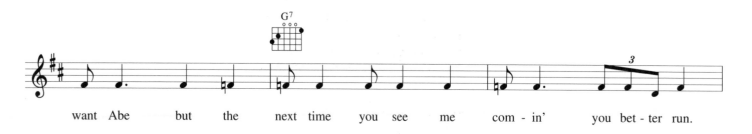

want Abe but the next time you see me com - in' you bet - ter run.

Well, Abe says, where do you want this

kill - in'   done?   God   says   out   on   High - way   Six - ty   -   one.

1 – 4. cont.   5.

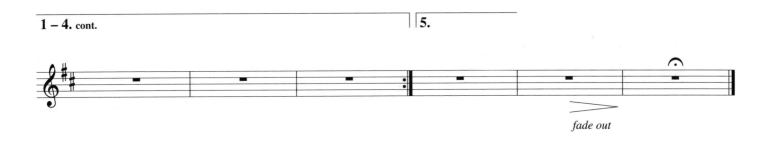

fade out

Verse 2:
Well Georgia Sam he had a bloody nose
Welfare Department they wouldn't give him no clothes
He asked poor Howard where can I go
Howard said there's only one place I know
Sam said tell me quick man I got to run
Ol' Howard just pointed with his gun
And said that way down on Highway 61.

Verse 3:
Well Mack the Finger said to Louie the King
I got forty red white and blue shoe strings
And a thousand telephones that don't ring
Do you know where I can get rid of these things
And Louie the King said let me think for a minute son
And he said yes I think it can be easily done
Just take everything down to Highway 61.

Verse 4:
Now the fifth daughter on the twelfth night
Told the first father that things weren't right
My complexion she said is much too white
He said come here and step into the light he says hmm you're right
Let me tell the second mother this has been done
But the second mother was with the seventh son
And they were both out on Highway 61.

Verse 5:
Now the rovin' gambler he was very bored
He was tryin' to create a next world war
He found a promoter who nearly fell off the floor
He said I never engaged in this kind of thing before
But yes I think it can be very easily done
We'll just put some bleachers out in the sun
And have it on Highway 61.

I Can See For Miles

Words & Music by Peter Townshend

1.4. I know you've de - ceived me, now here's a sur - prise.____

____ I know that you have, 'cause there's mag - ic in__ my eyes.__

____ I can see for miles and miles and miles and____

miles and____ miles,_____ oh yeah.____

47

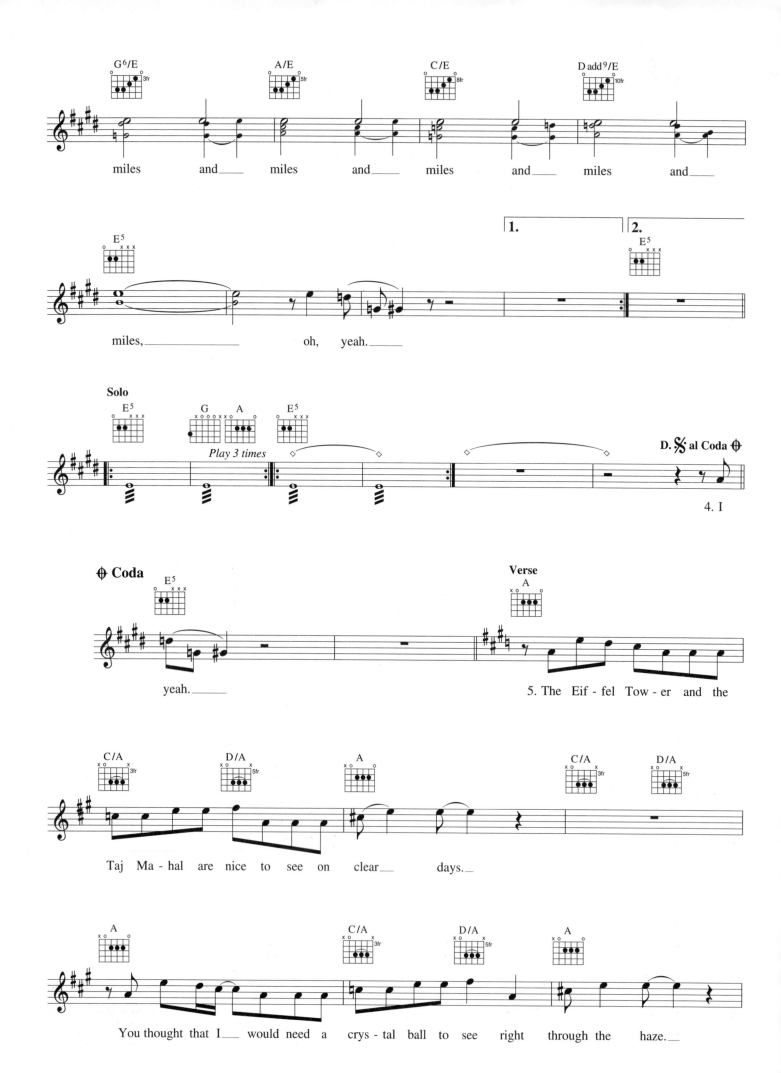

miles and miles and miles and miles and

miles, oh, yeah.

Solo

Play 3 times

D. 𝄌 al Coda ⊕

4. I

⊕ **Coda**

yeah.

Verse

5. The Eif - fel Tow - er and the

Taj Ma - hal are nice to see on clear days.

You thought that I would need a crys - tal ball to see right through the haze.

48

Well, here's a poke at you,___ you're gon-na choke on it too,___ you're gon-na

lose that smile___ be-cause all___ the while I can see for

miles, and miles, I can see for miles and miles, I can see for

miles and miles and miles and miles and

miles and miles and miles and miles.___

I can see for miles and miles. I can see for

49

Knowing Me, Knowing You

Words & Music by Benny Andersson, Stig Anderson & Bjorn Ulvaeus

1. No more____ care - free____ laugh - ter,____
(%) Mem' - ries,____ good days,____ bad days,____

si - lence____ ev - er____ af - ter._____ Walk -
they'll be____ with me____ al - ways._____ In____

- ing through an emp - ty house,____ tears in my eyes.____
____ these old fa - mil - iar rooms____ child - ren would play.____

This is where the sto - ry ends,____ this is good - bye.____
Now there's on - ly emp - ti - ness,____ no - thing to say.____

Hound Dog

Words & Music by Jerry Leiber & Mike Stoller

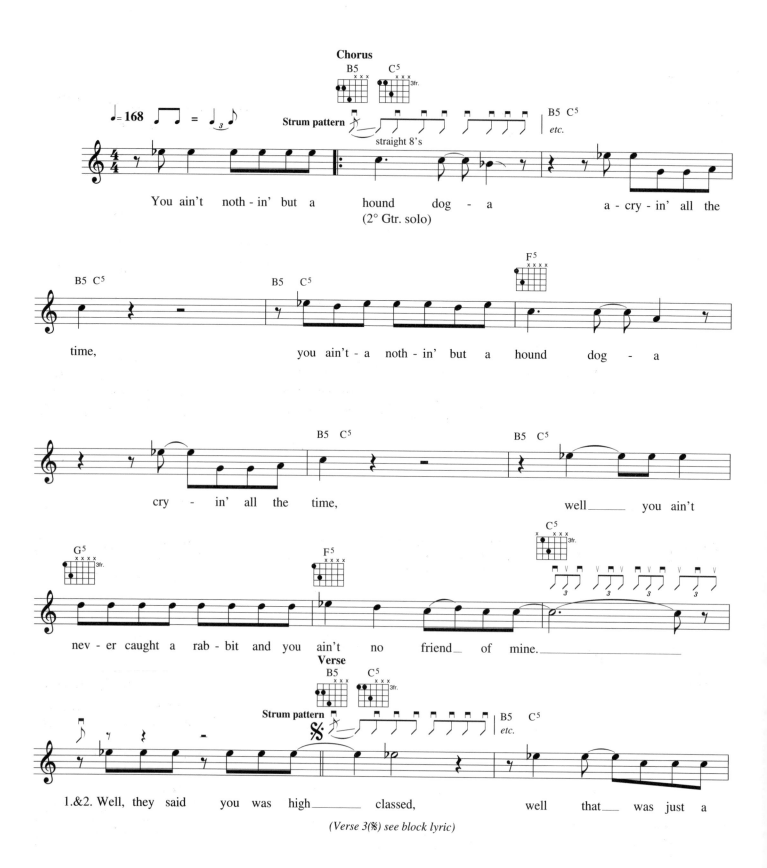

You ain't noth-in' but a hound dog - a a-cry-in' all the
(2° Gtr. solo)

time, you ain't - a noth-in' but a hound dog - a

cry - in' all the time, well_____ you ain't

nev - er caught a rab - bit and you ain't no friend_ of mine._____

1.&2. Well, they said you was high_____ classed, well that_ was just a

(Verse 3(%) see block lyric)

lie,   on (%) you know / yeah, they said   you was   high____ classed,

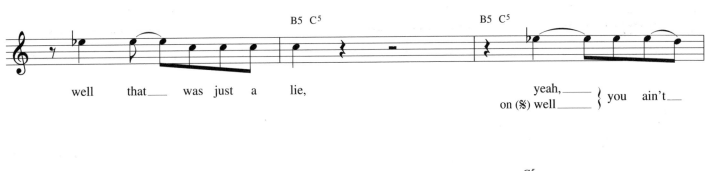

well   that____ was just a   lie,   on (%) well____ / yeah,____ you ain't____

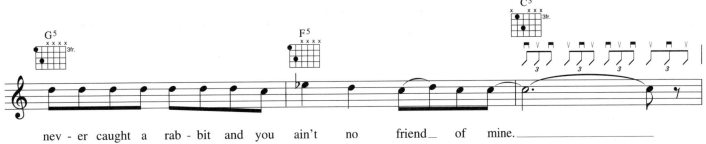

nev - er caught a rab - bit and you ain't   no   friend__ of mine._____

Chorus

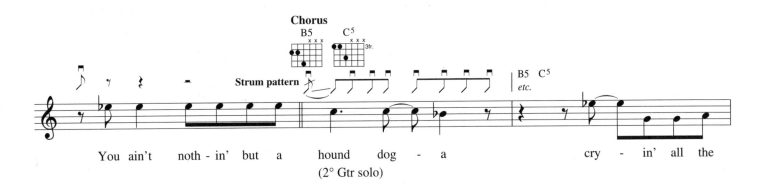

You ain't noth - in' but a   hound dog - a   cry - in' all the
(2° Gtr solo)

time,   you ain't 'n noth - in' but a   hound   dog - a____

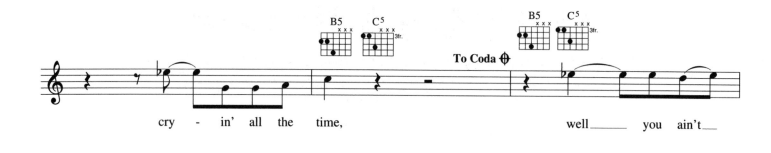

cry - in' all the time, well____ you ain't____

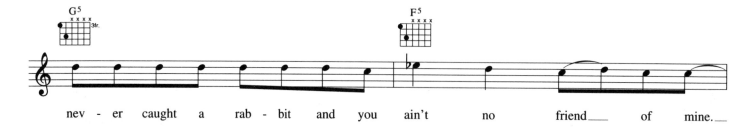

nev - er caught a rab - bit and you ain't no friend____ of mine.____

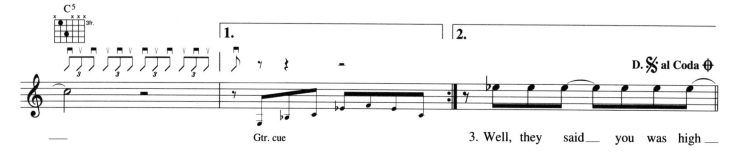

____ Gtr. cue 3. Well, they said____ you was high____

◉ Coda

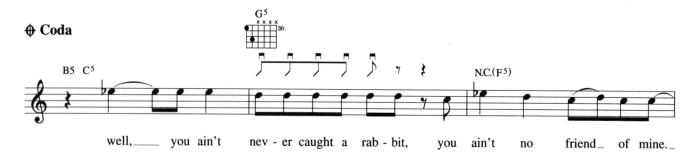

well,____ you ain't nev - er caught a rab - bit, you ain't no friend_ of mine._

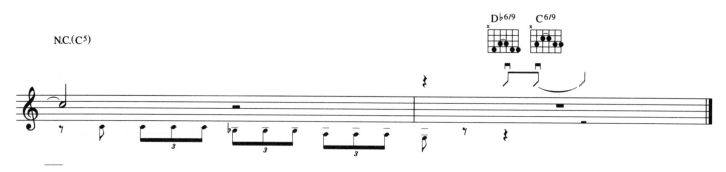

Verse 3(%):   Well, they said you was high classed
Well that was just a lie
You know they said you was high classed
Well that was just a lie
Well, you ain't never caught a rabbit
And you ain't no friend of mine.

Livin' On A Prayer

Words & Music by Jon Bon Jovi, Richie Sambora & Desmond Child

Verse 2:   Tommy got his six-string in hock
Now he's holding in when he used to talk
So tough it's tough.
Gena dreams of running away
When she cries in the night Tommy whispers
Baby it's O.K. some day.

Lady Madonna

Words & Music by John Lennon & Paul McCartney

Sun - day morn - ing creep - ing like a
Wednes - day morn - ing pa - pers did - n't
Ba, ba, ba, ba, _____ ba, ba,

nun. _____
come. _____
ba, ba, ba, _____ ba, ba.

Mon - day's child has
Thurs - day night your
Ba, ba, ba, ba,

learned to tie _____ his boot - lace. _____
stock - ings need - ed mend - ing. _____
ba, ba, ba, ba, ba, ba,) _____

See

how they run. _____

D. %. al Coda ⊕

⊕ Coda

59

Live Forever

Words & Music by Noel Gallagher

see,   you   and I___ are gon - na live   for - ev   -   er.

see,   you   and I___ are gon - na live   for - ev   -   er.   2. I said

Gon - na live   for - ev   -   er,___   gon - na live   for - ev -

- er,___   gon - na live   for - ev   -   er,___

___   gon - na live   for - ev   -   er,___   gon - na live   for - ev -

- er,___   gon - na live   for - ev   -   er.___

Lovefool

Words & Music by Peter Svensson & Nina Persson

1. Dear I feel we're fac-ing a prob-lem,
(Verse 2 see block lyric)

you love me no long-er, I know and may-be there is noth-

-ing that I can do, to make you do. Ma-ma tells me I

should-n't both-er, that I ought to stick to an-oth-er man,

a man that sure-ly de-serves me, I think you do.

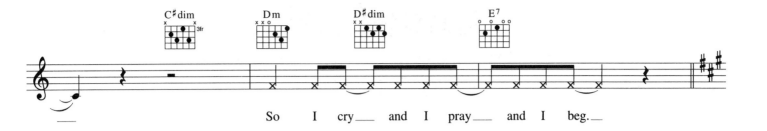

So I cry___ and I pray___ and I beg.___

Chorus

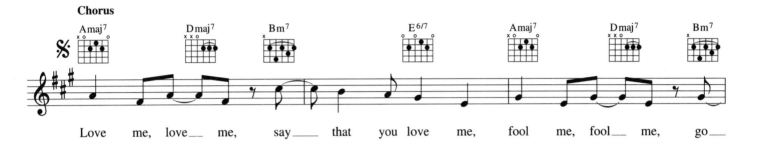

Love me, love___ me, say___ that you love me, fool me, fool___ me, go___

To Coda ✛

___ on and fool me, love me, love___ me, pre - tend___ that you love me,
I know___ that you need me,

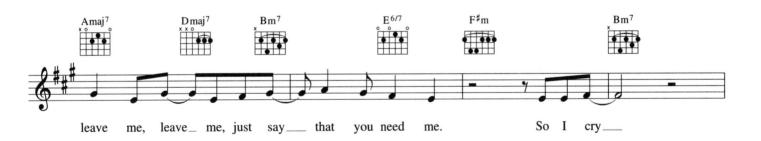

leave me, leave___ me, just say___ that you need me. So I cry___

and I beg___ for you to love me, love___ me, say___

63

_____ that you love me, leave me, leave _____ me, just say _____ that you need me,

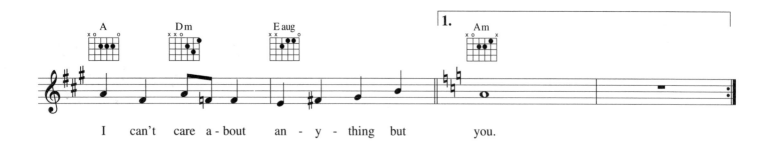

I can't care a - bout an - y - thing but you.

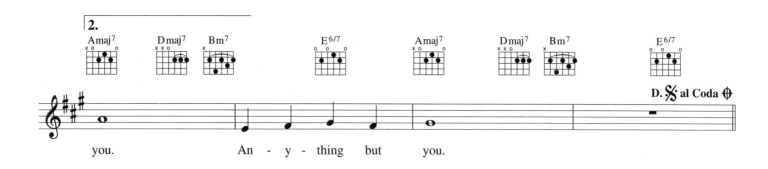

you. An - y - thing but you.

⊕ Coda

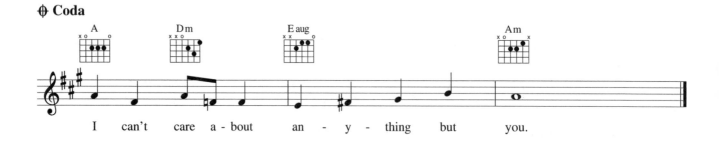

I can't care a - bout an - y - thing but you.

Verse 2:

Lately I have desperately pondered
Spent my nights awake and I wonder
What I could have done in another way
To make you stay.

Reason will not reach a solution
I will end up lost in confusion
I don't care if you really care
As long as you don't go.

Lucky You

Words & Music by Ian Broudie & Terry Hall

1. You're ly - ing a - gain, ___ you say you don't but

(Verses 2&3(%) see block lyric)

then you do. ___ I'm try - ing a - gain ___ to build ___ a wall

___ a - round ___ your heart ___ then break it through ___ to you, ___

you make it hap - pen. Ooh. ___

Ooh._____

Chorus

Ev - 'ry - thing's blue now,__ oh luck - y you.__ Oh luck - y__ you,__

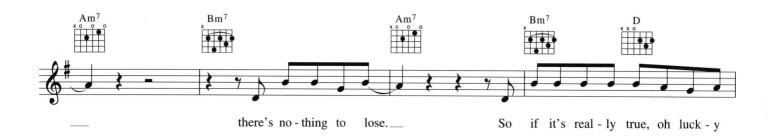

__ there's no - thing to lose.__ So if it's real - ly true, oh luck - y

1.

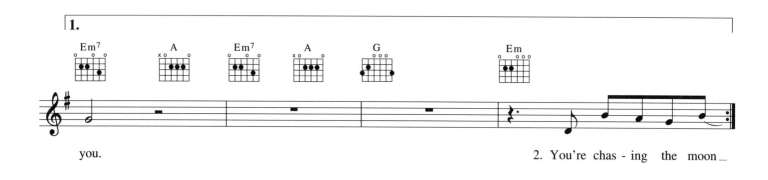

you. 2. You're chas - ing the moon__

2.3.(%)

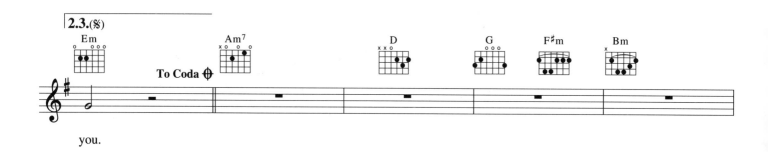

you.

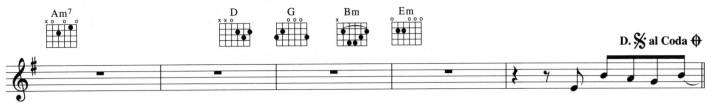

D. 𝄋 al Coda 𝄌

3. You're ly - ing a - gain,

𝄌 Coda

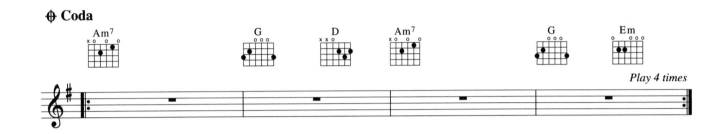

Play 4 times

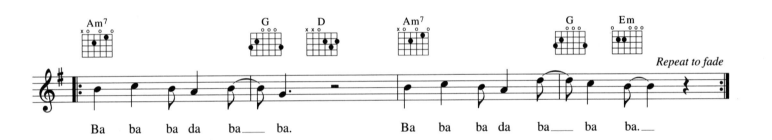

Repeat to fade

Ba   ba   ba da   ba____ ba.   Ba   ba   ba da   ba____ ba   ba.____

Verse 2:   You're chasing the moon
                  Reaching out to touch the stars
                  But you land too soon
                  What will it take to make you see
                  The way things really are?
                  You've got this far
                  So let it happen.

Verse 3:   You're lying again
                  Give it up and tell the truth
                  You can't stop the rain
                  It's gonna fall on every roof
                  I've got the proof
                  And only you can make it happen.

Massachusetts

Words & Music by Barry Gibb, Robin Gibb & Maurice Gibb

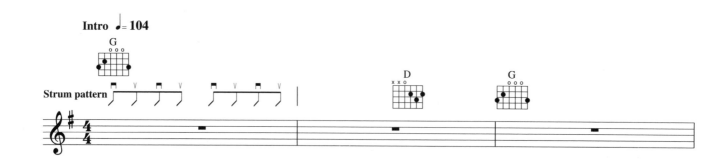

1. Feel I'm go-ing back to Mas-sa-
2. Tried to hitch a ride to San Fran-
3. Talk a-bout the life in Mas-sa-

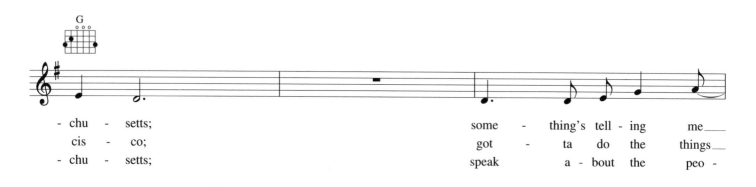

-chu-setts; some-thing's tell-ing me
cis-co; got-ta do the things
-chu-setts; speak a-bout the peo-

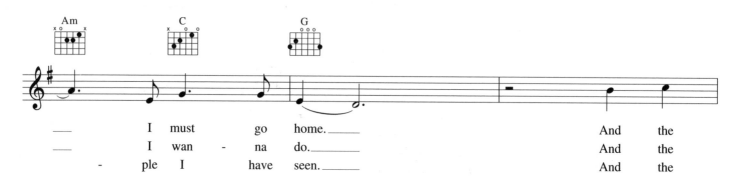

I must go home. And the
I wan-na do. And the
-ple I have seen. And the

lights   all   went   out   in   Mas   -   sa   -   chu   -   setts

lights   all   went   out   in   Mas   -   sa   -   chu   -   setts;

lights   all   went   out   in   Mas   -   sa   -   chu   -   setts;

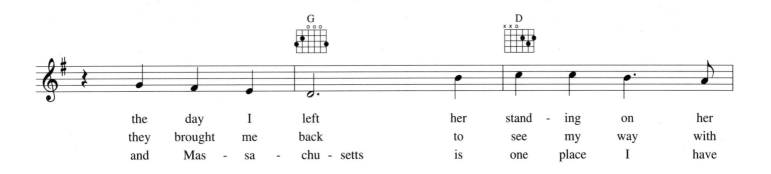

the   day   I   left   her   stand   -   ing   on   her

they   brought   me   back   to   see   my   way   with

and   Mas   -   sa   -   chu   -   setts   is   one   place   I   have

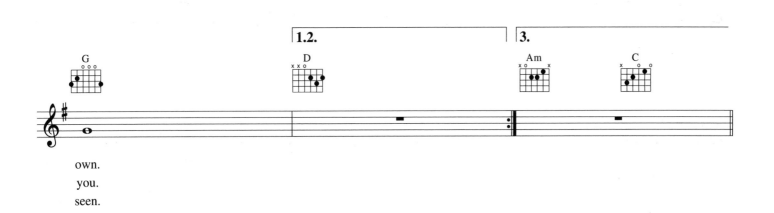

own.

you.

seen.

Outro

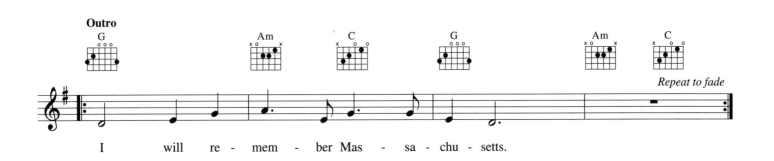

I   will   re   -   mem   -   ber   Mas   -   sa   -   chu   -   setts.

Repeat to fade

Metal Guru

Words & Music by Marc Bolan

Mr Tambourine Man

Words & Music by Bob Dylan

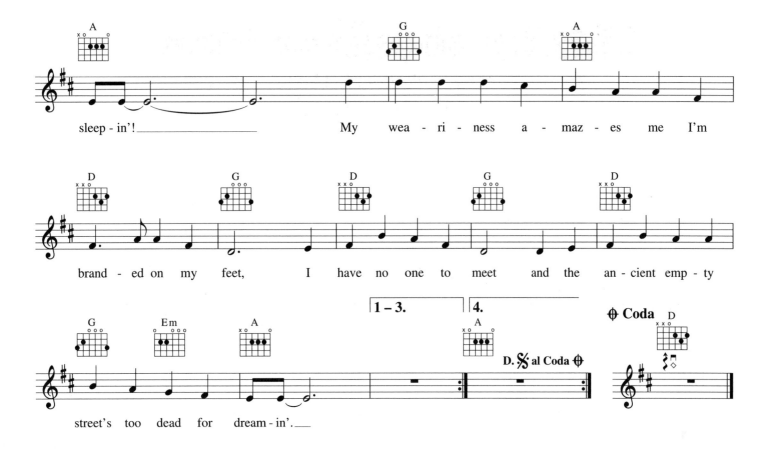

sleep - in'!_____ My wea - ri - ness a - maz - es me I'm

brand - ed on my feet, I have no one to meet and the an - cient emp - ty

|1 – 3. |4.   ⊕ Coda

D. 𝄋 al Coda ⊕

street's too dead for dream - in'.___

Chorus:

Verse 2:   Take me on a trip upon your magic swirlin' ship
My senses have been stripped, my hands can't feel the grip
My toes too numb to step, wait only for my boot heels
To be wanderin'
I'm ready to go anywhere, I'm ready for to fade
Into my own parade, cast your dancin' spell my way
I promise to go under it.

Chorus:

Verse 3:   Though you might hear laughin' spinnin' swingin' madly across the sun
It's not aimed at anyone, it's just escapin' on the run
And but for the sky there are no fences facin'
And if you hear vague traces of skippin' reels of rhyme
To your tambourine in time, it's just a ragged clown behind
I wouldn't pay it any mind, it's just a shadow you're
Seein' that he's chasin'.

Chorus:

Verse 4:   Then take me disappearin' through the smoke rings of my mind
Down the foggy ruins of time, far past the frozen leaves
The haunted, frightened trees out to the windy beach
Far from the twisted reach of crazy sorrow
Yes, to dance beneath the diamond sky with one hand wavin' free
Silhouetted by the sea, circled by the circus sands
With all memory and fate driven deep beneath the waves
Let me forget about today until tomorrow.

Chorus:

Money, Money, Money

Words & Music by Benny Andersson & Bjorn Ulvaeus

Intro ♩ = 124

Verse

work all night, I work all day to pay the bills I have to pay,___ ain't it sad.___
man like that is hard to find, but I can't get him off my mind,___ ain't it sad.___

___ And still there nev - er seems to be a sin - gle pen - ny left for me,___
___ And if he hap - pens to be free I bet he would - n't fan - cy me,___

that's too bad.___ In my dreams___ I have a plan,___
that's too bad.___ So I must leave,___ I'll have to go

Mull Of Kintyre

Words & Music by McCartney & Laine

Past paint - ed des - erts___ the sun - set's on fire as he car - ries me home___

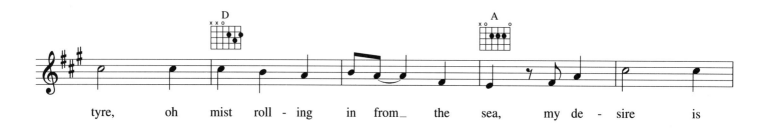

Chorus

___ to the Mull of Kin - tyre. Mull of Kin -

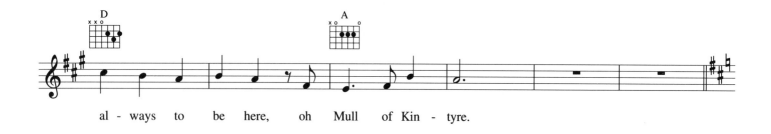

tyre, oh mist roll - ing in from___ the sea, my de - sire is

al - ways to be here, oh Mull of Kin - tyre.

Bagpipe solo

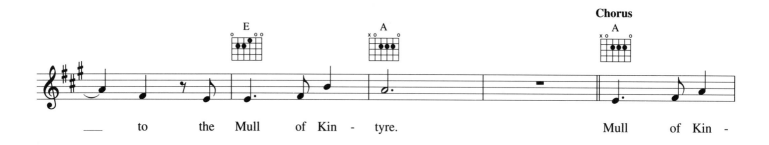

My Generation

Words & Music by Pete Townshend

talk - in' 'bout my g-gen - er - a - tion._____ Ba - by, my__ gen - er - a -

Chorus

- tion,___ this is my__ gen - er - a - tion, ba - by._____

My, my, ge - gen - er - a - tion. My, my, ooh, my, my.

Verse

1° My, my, my, gen - er - a - tion. Peo - ple try to put us d-down___

just be - cause we g-g-g-get a - round.___
(Talk - in' 'bout my gen - er - a - tion.)

Things they do look aw - ful c-c-cold,_____

Need You Tonight

Words & Music by Andrew Farriss & Michael Hutchence

1. All you get is this mo - ment,____
(Verses 2–3(%) see block lyric)

the twen - ty first cen - tury's yes - ter - day,____ you can care all you want____

—— ev - 'ry - bo - dy does, yeah that's O. K.____

1.

So slide ov - er here____ and give me a mo - ment, your

Night Fever

Words & Music by Barry Gibb, Robin Gibb & Maurice Gibb

1. Lis - ten to the ground: there is move - ment all a - round. There is
2. heat of our love, don't need no help for us to make it. Gim - me

some - thing go - in' down, and I can feel it. On the
just e - nough to take us to the morn - in'. I got

waves of the air, there is danc - in' out there. If it's
fire on my mind. I got high - er in my walk - in'. And I'm

some - thin' we can share, we can steal it. }
glow - in' in the dark; I give you warn - in'. }

And that

89

No Particular Place To Go

Words & Music by Chuck Berry

1. Ri - din' a - long in my au - to - mo - bile, _____ my ba - by be - side me at the wheel,

(Verse 3 see block lyric)

I stole a kiss at the turn of a mile, my cu - ri - os - i - ty run - nin' wild, _____ cruis - in' and play - in' the ra - di - o, with no par - tic - u - lar place to go. _____ 2. Ri - din' a - long in my au - to - mo -

Verse

- bile,   I's anx - ious to tell her the way I   feel.

(Verse 4 see block lyric)

So I told her soft - ly and sin - cere, ____   and she leaned and whis - pered in my

ear.   Cud - dl - in' more and driv - in' slow,

To Coda

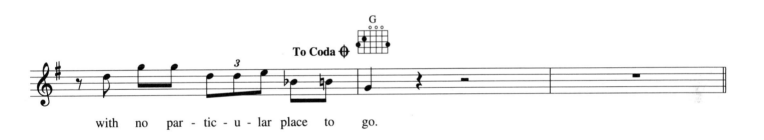

with no par - tic - u - lar place to   go.

Solo

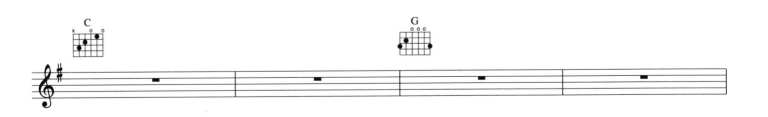

91

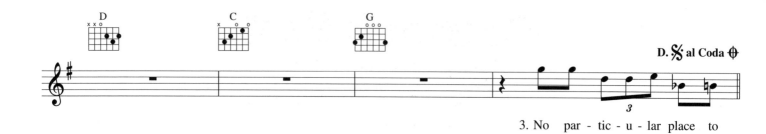

D. 𝄋 al Coda ⊕

3. No par - tic - u - lar place to

⊕ Coda

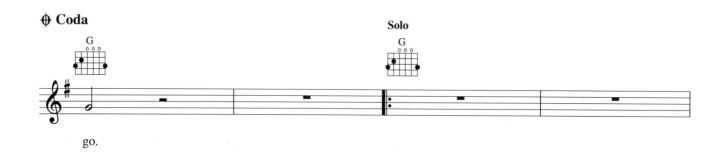

go.

Ad lib solo to fade

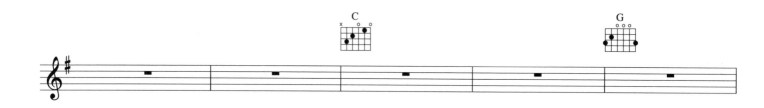

Verse 3(𝄋):   No particular place to go
          So we parked way out on the Kokomo
          The night was young and the moon was gold
          So we both decided to take a stroll
          Can you imagine the way I felt
          I couldn't unfasten the safety belt.

Verse 4:   Riding along in my calaboose
          Still tryin' to get her belt unloose
          All the way home I felt a grudge
          For the safety belt that wouldn't budge
          Cruisin' and playin' the radio
          With no particular place to go.

Peacock Suit

Words & Music by Paul Weller

ruf - fle the fea - thers of my pea - cock suit,_____ my pea - cock suit._

_____ 2. I'm Nar - did you think I should?_____

In my Pea - cock suit,_____ I look real cute._____

3. Ne - me - sis in a mud - dle, in a

mir - ror I look._____ Like a streak of sheet light - nin'_____ in my

rat - tle - snake shoes. _____ I don't need a ship to sail ___

___ in storm - y wea - ther, don't __ need you __ to ruf - fle the fea - thers of my __

pea - cock suit, _____ d'ya think I care? _____

in my pea - cock suit, _____

did you think I should? _____

Outro

Pea - cock suit, _

Repeat ad lib to fade

_____ yeah. _____ Pea - cock suit, _____ yeah. _____

95

One Way

Words & Music by Simon Friend, Charles Kenton Heather, Mark Chadwick, Johnathan Sevink & Jeremy James Cunningham

There's on - ly one ___ way of life, ___ and that's ___ your own, ___ your own, your own. ___

1. My

fa - ther, when I was young - er took me up on - to ___ the hill ___ that looked

(Verse 2 see block lyric)

down on the ci - ty smog ___ and a - bove the fac - to - ry spill. ___ He said, 'Now

this is   where___   I come___   when I   want   to be   free.’___   Well he

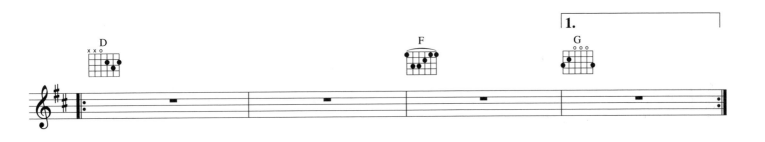

nev - er   was___   in his___   life - time,   but   these   words   stuck   with   me.___   Hey!

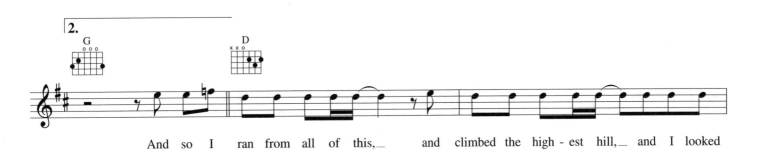

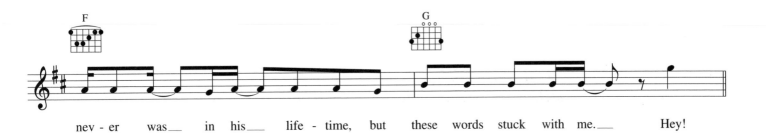

And so   I   ran from   all of   this,___   and   climbed   the high - est   hill,___   and I   looked

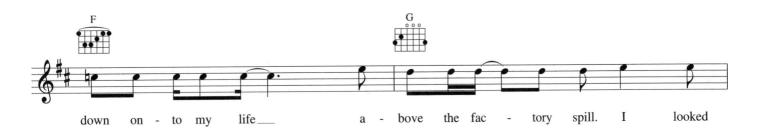

down   on - to   my   life___   a - bove   the fac - tory   spill.   I   looked

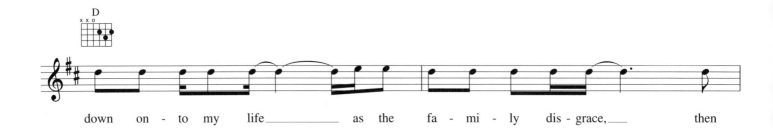

down on-to my life_____ as the fa - mi - ly dis - grace,___ then

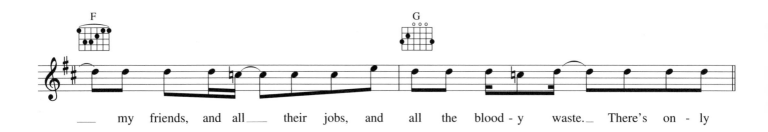

all my friends on the start - ing line their wa - ges off to chase._ Yes, and all__

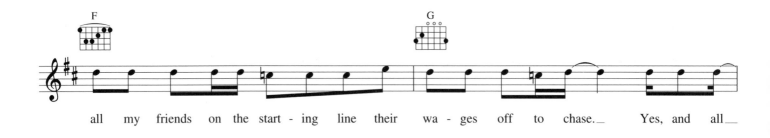

___ my friends, and all___ their jobs, and all the blood - y waste._ There's on - ly

Chorus

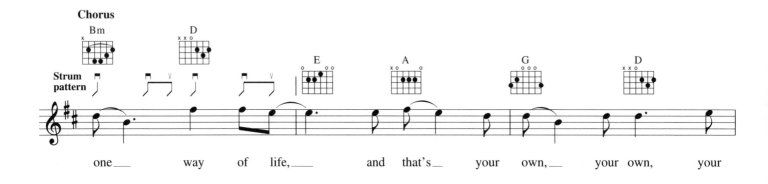

one___ way of life,___ and that's___ your own,___ your own, your

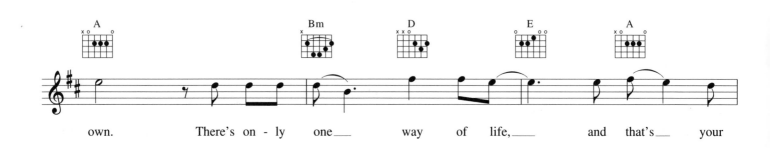

own. There's on - ly one___ way of life,___ and that's___ your

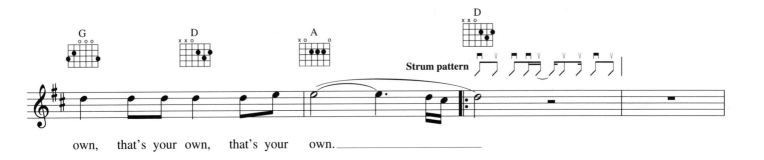

own,　　that's your own,　　that's your　　own. _____

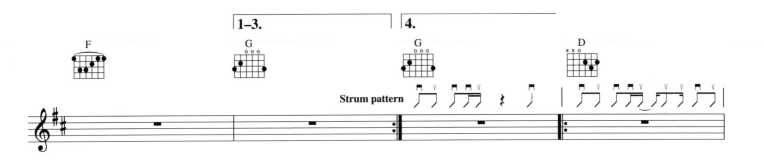

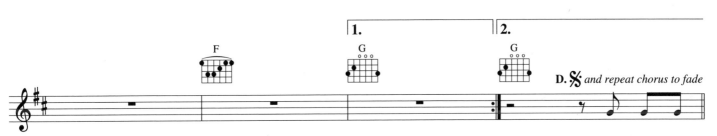

2. Well, well, well,

Verse 2:　　　　Well, well, well
I grew up, learned to love and laugh,
Circled As on the underpass
But the noise we thought would never stop
Died a death as the punks grew up
And we choked on our dreams
We wrestled with our fears
We're running through the heartless concrete streets
Chasing our ideas. Run!

And the problems of the world
Won't be solved by this guitar
And they won't stop coming either
By the life I've had so far
And the bright lights of my home town
Won't be getting any dimmer
Though their calling has receded
Like some old distant singer
And they don't look so appealing
To the eyes of this poor sinner.

Repeat *Chorus* (twice)

Out Of The Sinking

Words & Music by Paul Weller

Chorus

(Chorus 2 see block lyric)

1. Hey ba - by say just__ what you're think - ing.__ Know__ I know it

yeah,__ feel I'm sink - ing. Know__ I feel it, know__ you feel it too.__

A - cross the wa - ter,__ there's a boat that__ will take us a - way.__

Is it shout - ing for me?_____

All I need it to be._____ But I can't find the key,__

101

the one to make me be - lieve,

Solo

D. 𝄌 al Coda ⊕

⊕ Coda

Out of the sad - ness far from the mad - ness,

in - to sun - light yeah, out of a sink - ing. Know I feel it,

Strum pattern

I know you feel it too. A-cross the wa - ter, there's a boat that

will take us a - way,_____   there we'll   stay._____

But I can't find the key._

Verse 2(%):
Late at night
When the world is dreaming
Way past the stars
That ignore our fate
And all twinkle too late to save us
So we save ourselves.

Chorus 2:
Hey baby, do just what you're thinking
Know I know it, yeah, feel I'm sinking
Know I feel it, I know you feel it too
Across the water is a boat that will take us away.

Roll With It

Words & Music by Noel Gallagher

You got-ta roll___ with it, you got-ta take___ you time, you got-ta say___ what you say,___ don't let an-y-bo-dy get in your way, 'cause it's all___ too much___ for me to take.___ Don't ev-er stand___ a-side don't ev-er be de-nied,___ you wan-na

be__ who you'd be__ if you're com - in' with me.__ I think I've got a feel - in' I've lost__

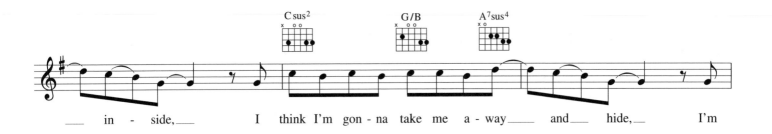

__ in - side,__ I think I'm gon - na take me a - way__ and__ hide,__ I'm

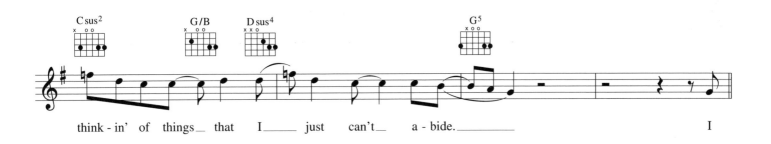

think - in' of things__ that I__ just can't__ a - bide._____ I

Bridge

know__ the roads__ down which__ your life__ will drive,__ I'll

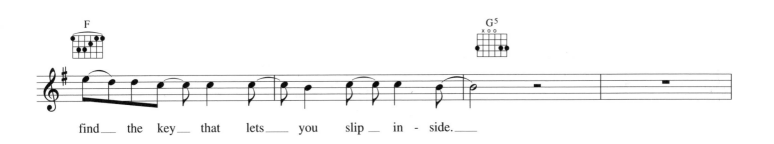

find__ the key__ that lets__ you slip__ in - side.__

Kiss___ the girl,___ she's not___ be - hind___ the door,_____ but you

know I think I rec - og - nise____ your face___ but I've nev - er seen you be - fore.

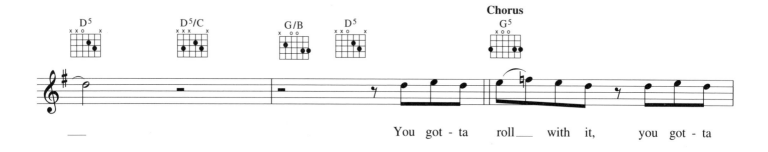

Chorus

___ You got - ta roll___ with it, you got - ta

take___ your time, you got - ta say___ what you say,___ don't let an - y - bo - dy get in your way,

'cause it's all___ too much___ for me to take.___

Solo

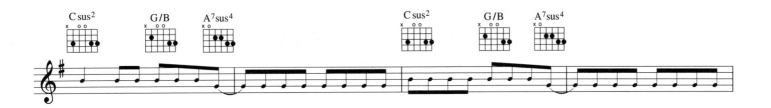

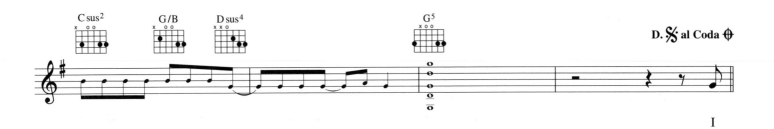

D. 𝄋 al Coda ⟡

I

⟡ Coda

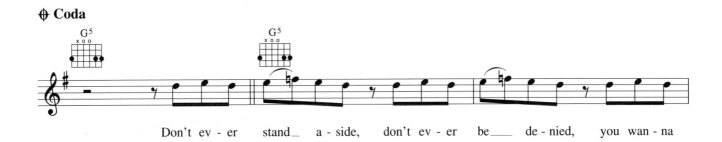

Don't ev - er stand__ a - side, don't ev - er be__ de - nied, you wan - na

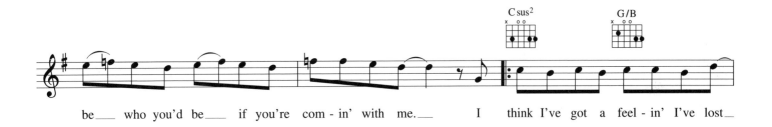

be__ who you'd be__ if you're com - in' with me.__ I think I've got a feel - in' I've lost__

1.2.3.

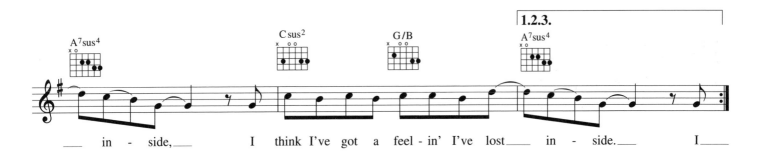

__ in - side,__ I think I've got a feel - in' I've lost__ in - side.__ I__

4.

Play 3 times

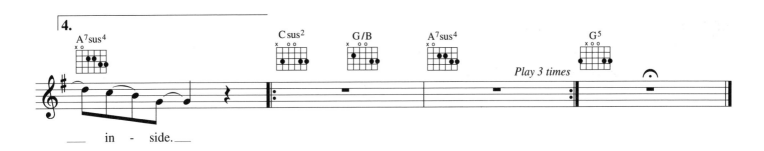

__ in - side.__

107

Road Rage

Words & Music by Cerys Matthews & Mark Roberts

If all you've got to do today is find peace of mind,

come 'round you can take a piece of mine.

And if all you've got to do today is he-si-tate,

come here, you can leave it late with me.

You could be tak-ing it ea-sy on your-self, you should be mak-ing it ea-

- sy on___ your - self.___ 'Cause you and I___ know it's all ov - er the front___

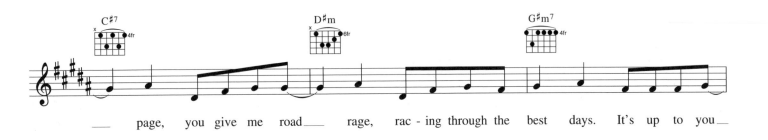

___ page, you give me road___ rage, rac - ing through the best days. It's up to you___

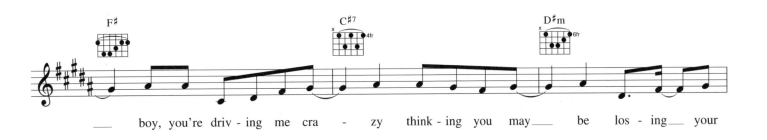

___ boy, you're driv - ing me cra - zy think - ing you may___ be los - ing___ your

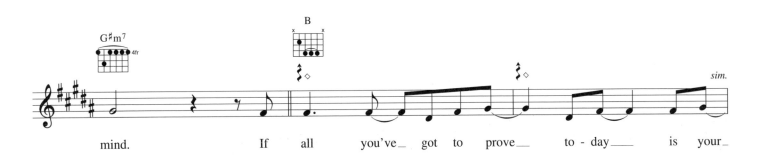

mind. If all you've___ got to prove___ to - day___ is your___

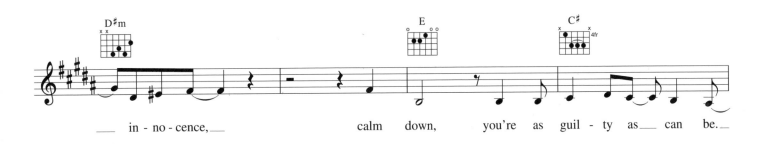

___ in - no - cence,___ calm down, you're as guil - ty as___ can be.___

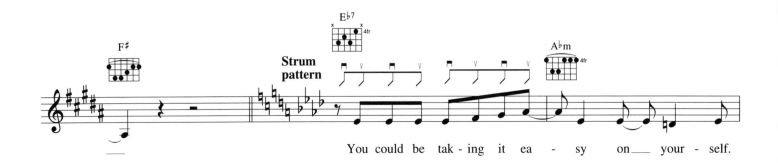

You could be tak - ing it ea - sy on___ your - self.

You should be mak - ing it ea - sy on___ your - self.___ 'Cause you and I___ know

Chorus

it's all ov - er the front___ page, you give me road___ rage, rac - ing through the

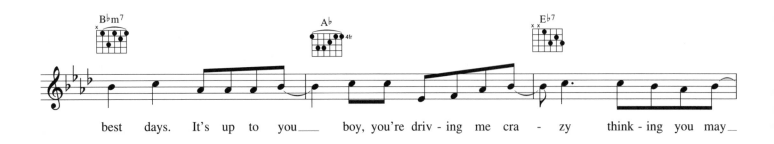

best days. It's up to you___ boy, you're driv - ing me cra - zy think - ing you may___

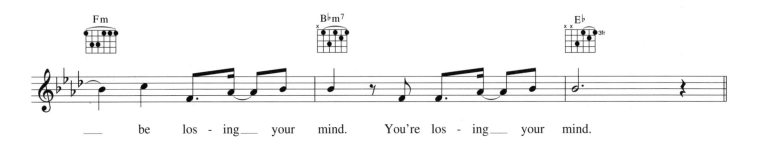

___ be los - ing___ your mind. You're los - ing___ your mind.

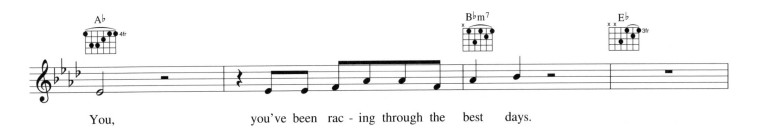

You,   you've been rac - ing through the best days.

Space age, road rage, fast lane. And if all_____ you've__ got to do__

_____ to - day___ is find___ peace of mind___   come here,___ you__ can

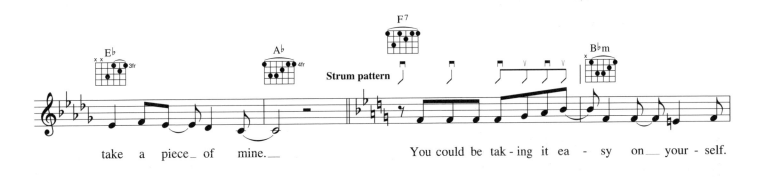

take a piece__ of mine.___   You could be tak - ing it ea - sy on___ your - self.

You should be mak - ing it ea - sy on___ your - self.___ 'Cause you and I__ know

it's all ov - er the front___ page, you give me road___ rage, rac - ing through the

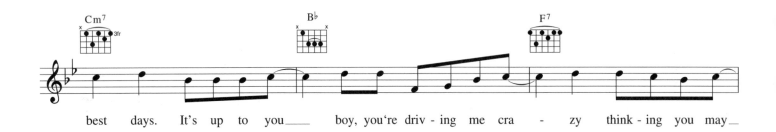

best days. It's up to you___ boy, you're driv - ing me cra - zy think - ing you may___

___ be los - ing___ your mind. But you and I___ know we all live in the space___

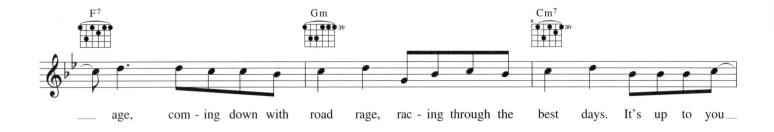

___ age, com - ing down with road rage, rac - ing through the best days. It's up to you___

___ boy, you're driv - ing me cra - zy think - ing you may___ be los - ing___ your mind.

Repeat ad lib to fade

It's not ov - er, it's not ov - er,___ it's not ov - er.

Saturday Night's Alright
For Fighting

Words & Music by Elton John & Bernie Taupin

1. It's get - ting late, ____ have you seen my mates? ____ Ma,
(2.) packed pret - ty tight in ____ here to - night; ____ I'm

tell me when the boys get here. ____ It's sev - en o' - clock ____ and I
look - ing for a dolly to see me right. I may use a lit - tle mus - cle to

wan - na rock, wan - na get a bel - ly full of beer. My
get what I need, I may sink a lit - tle drink and shout out "She's with me!" A

old man's drunk - er than a bar - rel full of mon - keys and my old la - dy, she don't
couple of sounds that I real - ly like are the sounds of a switch - blade and a

care. My sis - ter looks cute in her brac - es and boots, ____ a
motorbike. I'm a ju - ven - ile product of the work - ing class ____ whose

113

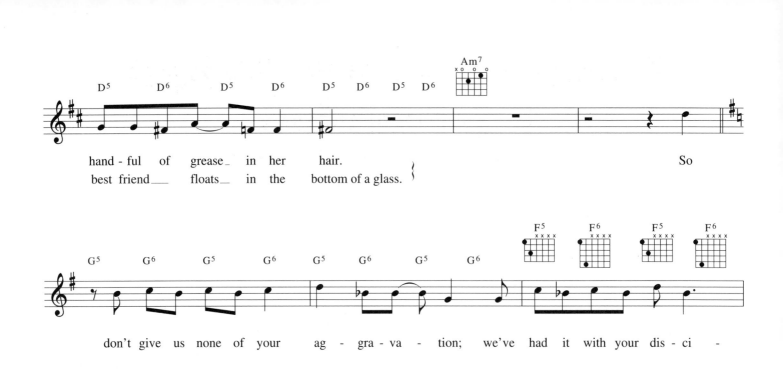

hand - ful of grease_ in her hair.
best friend___ floats_ in the bottom of a glass.

So

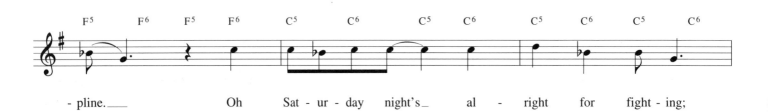

don't give us none of your ag - gra - va - tion; we've had it with your dis - ci -

- pline.___ Oh Sat - ur - day night's_ al - right for fight - ing;

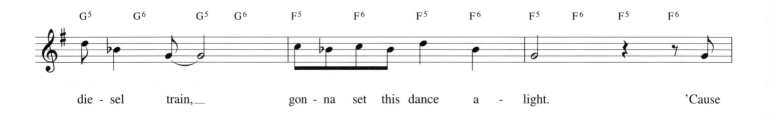

get a lit - tle ac - tion___ in. Get a - bout as oiled_ as a

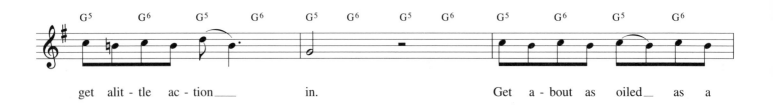

die - sel train,_ gon - na set this dance a - light. 'Cause

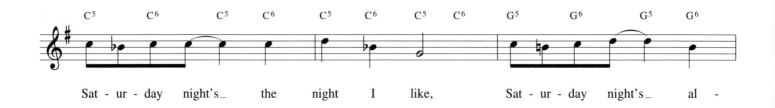

Sat - ur - day night's_ the night I like, Sat - ur - day night's_ al -

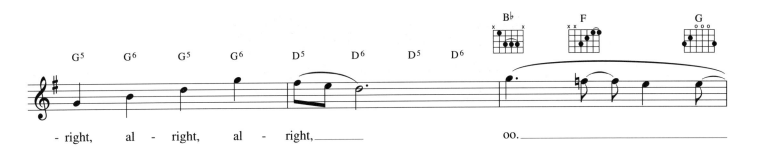

- right,   al - right,   al - right,_____   oo._____

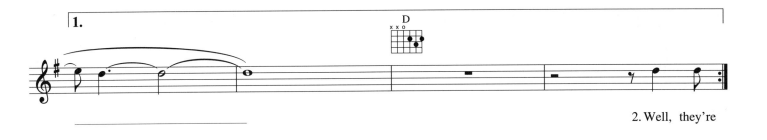

2. Well, they're

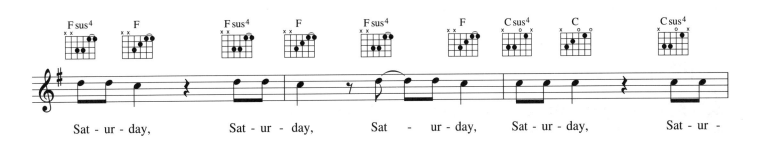

Sat - ur - day,   Sat - ur - day,   Sat - ur - day,

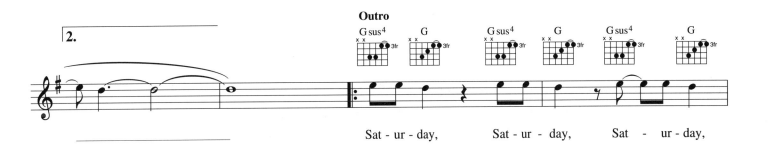

Sat - ur - day,   Sat - ur - day,   Sat - ur - day,   Sat - ur - day,   Sat - ur -

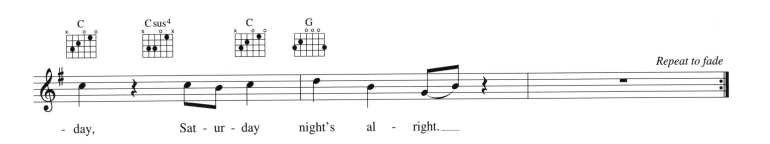

Repeat to fade

- day,   Sat - ur - day   night's al - right.___

Space Oddity

Words & Music by David Bowie

look ve - ry   dif - fer - ent   to - day._____   For

Bridge

here   am I   sit - ting in a tin   can,____
(𝄋)(hear me)   (𝄋)(float - ing round my)

far _____   a - bove____   the world.____
                                        (the moon.)____

Plan - et earth__ is blue   and there's no - thing I can do._____

Strum pattern

Strum pattern

To Coda ⊕

118

Though I'm past one hun- dred thou- sand miles ___ I'm feel- ing ve- ry still, ___

___ and I think my space- ship knows which way to go. ___

___ Tell my wife I love her ve- ry much, she knows. ___

___ Ground Con- trol to Ma- jor Tom, ___ your ___

cir- cuit's dead, there's some- thing wrong, can you hear me Ma- jor Tom, ___ can you

hear me Ma- jor Tom, ___ can you hear me Ma- jor Tom? ___ Can you

D. %: al Coda ⊕

⊕ Coda

Repeat ad lib to fade

Ten Storey Love Song

Words & Music by John Squire

Chorus

Ten stor - ey love song, I built this thing for you, ooh. Who can take you high - er than twin peak moun - tain blue? Oh well, I built this thing for you, and I love you true.

2. There's no

Solo

D.S. al Coda **Coda**

love you true.

121

The Circle

Words & Music by Simon Fowler, Steve Cradock,
Oscar Harrison & Damon Minchella

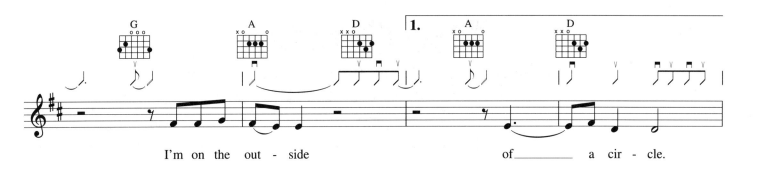

I'm on the out - side of_____ a cir - cle.

1. cont.

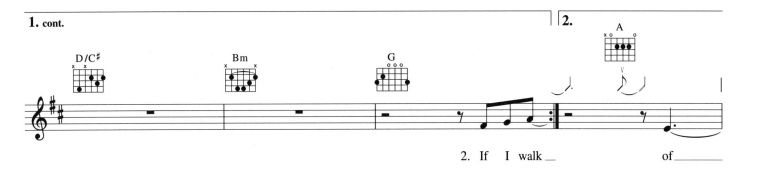

2. If I walk__ of_____

Bridge

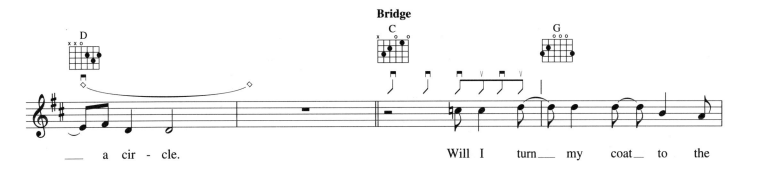

___ a cir - cle. Will I turn__ my coat__ to the

rain? I don't know. But I'm go - ing some -

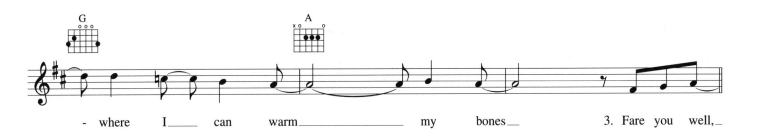

- where I___ can warm_____ my bones__ 3. Fare you well,__

123

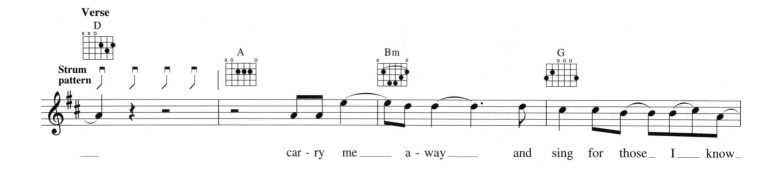

car-ry me____ a-way____ and sing for those_ I__ know_

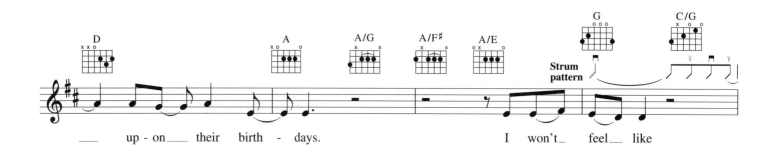

____ up-on____ their birth - days. I won't_ feel_ like

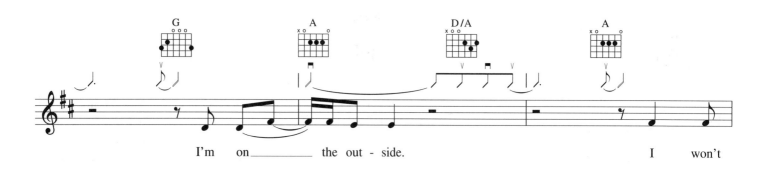

I'm on_____ the out - side. I won't

feel_ like I'm on the out - side, I won't

feel like I'm on the out - side of_____

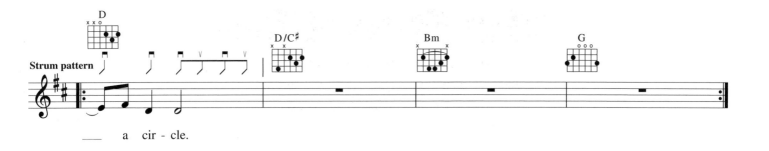

_ a   cir - cle.

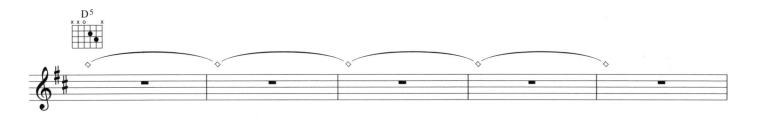

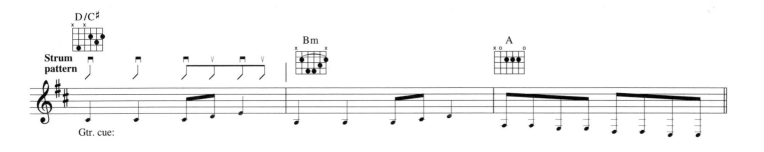

Gtr. cue:

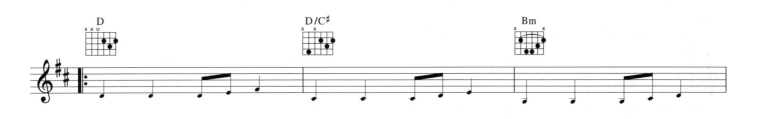

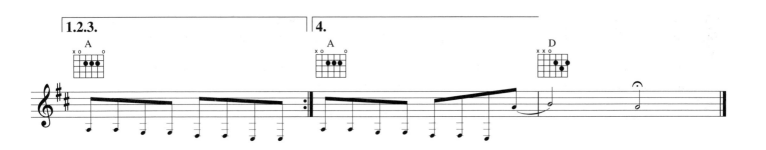

The Eton Rifles

Words & Music by Paul Weller

1. Sup up your beer and col-lect your fags,___ there's a row go-ing on
2. Thought you were smart when you took them on ___ but you did-n't take a peep in their ar-

(Verses 3 & 4(%) see block lyric)

down near Slough. Get out your mat and pray ___ to the west,___
-till-er-y room. All that rug-by puts hairs ___ on your chest,___ what

I'll get out mine and pray _____ for my - self. _____
chance have you got a - gainst a tie and a crest. _____

Chorus

Hel - lo hur - ray, what a nice day for the E - ton Ri - fles,
(Chorus 2 see block lyric)

E - ton Ri - fles. Hel - lo hur - ray, I hope rain stops play with the

E - ton Ri - fles, E - ton Ri - fles.

What a cat - a - lyst you turned out to be, load - ed your guns then you

ran off home _____ for your tea, _____ Left me stand - ing like a

guilt - y school - boy. _____

What a cat - a - lyst you turned out to be, load - ed your guns then you

ran off home__ for your tea,__ Left me stand - ing like a

D. % al Coda ⊕

guilt - y school - boy._____

⊕ **Coda**

Hel - lo hur - rah there's a price to pay to the

E - ton Ri - fles E - ton Ri - fles. Hel - lo hur - ray, I'd pre -

- fer the plague to the E - ton Ri - fles E - ton Ri - fles.

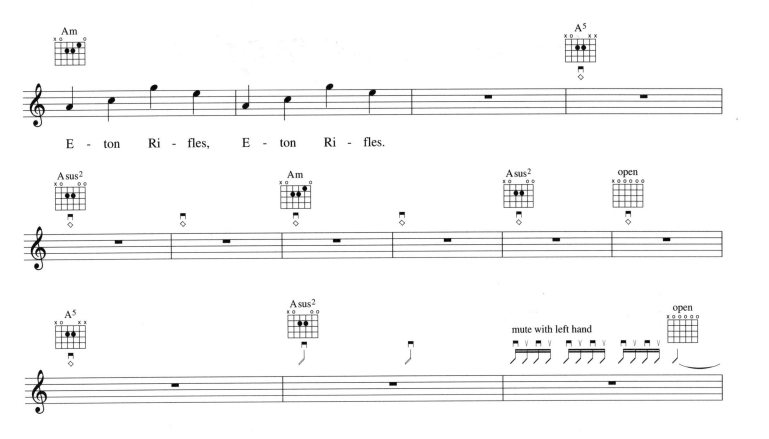

E - ton Ri - fles, E - ton Ri - fles.

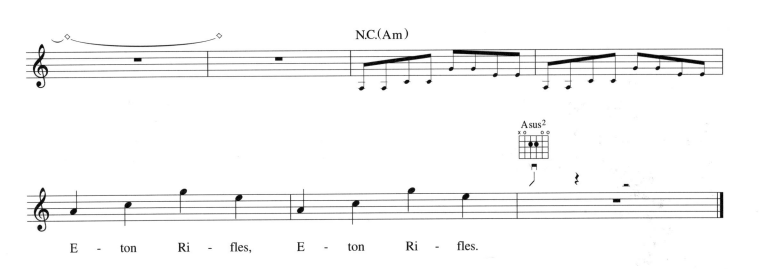

E - ton Ri - fles, E - ton Ri - fles.

Verse 3:   Thought you were clever when you lit the fuse
              Tore down the House of Commons in your brand new shoes
              Compose a revolutionary symphony
              Then went to bed with a charming young thing.

Chorus 2:   Hello hurray, cheers then mate, it's the Eton Rifles
              Hello hurray, an extremist scrape, with the Eton Rifles.

Verse 4(𝄋)   We came out of it naturally the worst
              Beaten and bloody I was sick down my shirt
              We were no match for their untamed wit
              Though some of the lads said they'd be back next week.

129

Town Called Malice

Words & Music by Paul Weller

1. Bet - ter stop dream - ing of the qui - et life____ cos it's the
2. Rows and rows of dis - used____ milk floats stand

(Verse 4(%) see block lyric)

one we'll nev - er know.____ Quit run - ning for that run
dy - ing in the dairy yard. And a hun - dred lone - ly house -

a - way bus 'cos those ros - y days____ are few____ well.____
wives clutch emp - ty milk bot - tles to their hearts.

big de - cis - ion in a town called Mal - ice._____

Ooh ooh yeah.____

Ooh - ooh.____

D. 𝄋 al Coda ⊕

⊕ Coda

Mal - ice, yeah.____

Ooh._____

Repeat to fade

Verse 4(𝄋):   The ghost of a steam train
Echoes down my track
It's at the moment bound for nowhere
Just going round and round
Playground kids and creaking swings
Lost laughter in the breeze
I could go on for hours
And I probably will
But I'd sooner put some joy back
In this town called Malice.

Trash

Words & Music by Brett Anderson & Richard Oakes

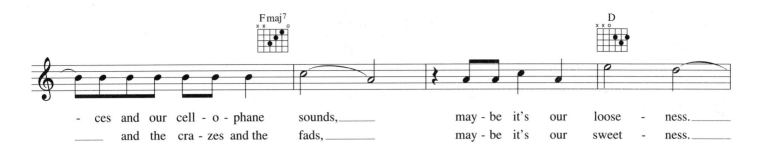

- ces and our cell - o - phane sounds,_____ may - be it's our loose - ness._____
_____ and the cra - zes and the fads,_____ may - be it's our sweet - ness._____

Chorus

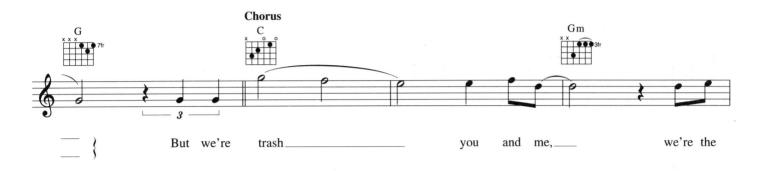

___ But we're trash_____ you and me,____ we're the

lit - ter on the breeze,___ we're the lov - ers on the streets.___

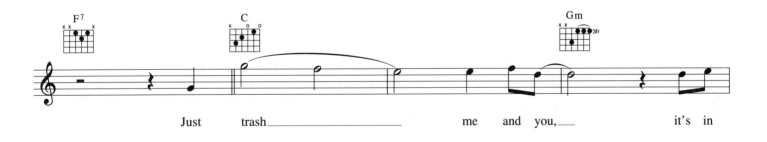

Just trash_____ me and you,____ it's in

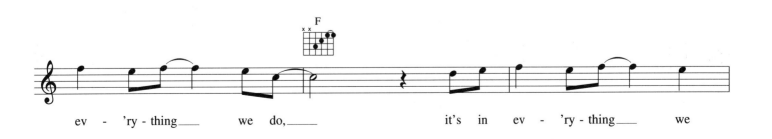

ev - 'ry - thing___ we do,____ it's in ev - 'ry - thing___ we

2 Become 1

Words & Music by Victoria Aadams, Melanie Brown, Emma Bunton, Melanie Chisholm, Geri Halliwell, Matt Rowe & Richard Stannard

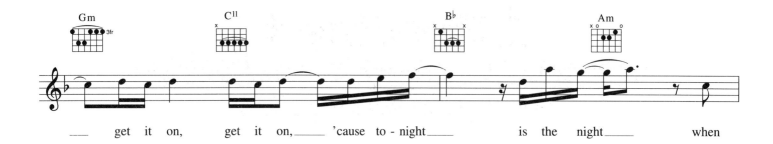

_____ get it on,   get it on, _____ 'cause to - night _____ is the night _____ when

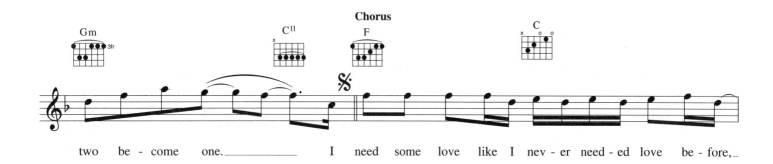

two be - come one. _____   I need some love like I nev - er need - ed love be - fore, _____

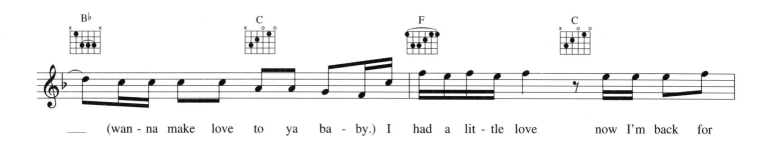

_____ (wan - na make love to ya ba - by.) I had a lit - tle love   now I'm back for

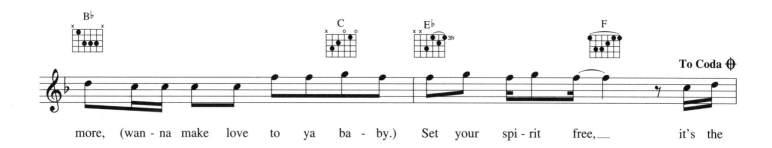

more, (wan - na make love to ya ba - by.) Set your spi - rit free, _____   it's the

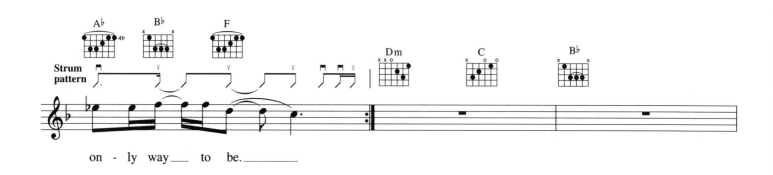

on - ly way _____ to be. _____

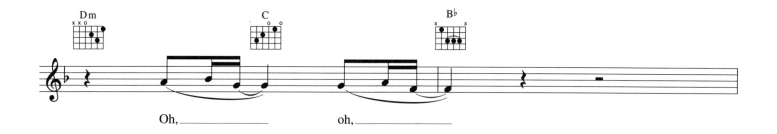

Oh,_____ oh,_____

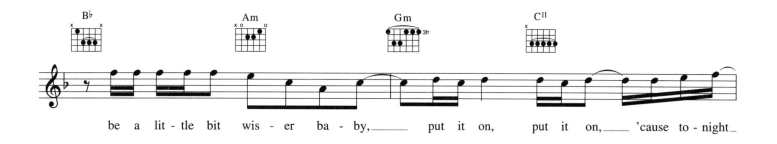

be a lit - tle bit wis - er ba - by,_____ put it on, put it on,_____ 'cause to - night_

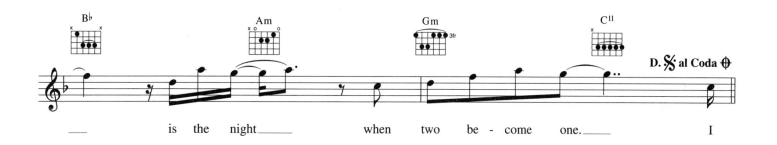

D. 𝄋 al Coda 𝄌

_____ is the night_____ when two be - come one._____ I

𝄌 Coda

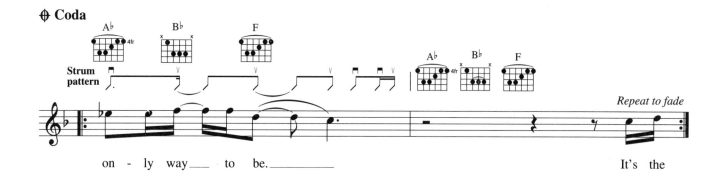

Strum
pattern

Repeat to fade

on - ly way____ to be._____ It's the

Verse 2: Silly games that you were playing, empty words we both were saying
Let's work it out boy, let's work it out boy
Any deal that we endeavour, boys and girls feel good together
Take it or leave it, take it or leave it
Are you as good as I remember baby, get it on, get it on
'Cause tonight is the night when two become one.

I need some love like I never needed love before, (wanna make love to ya baby)
I had a little love, now I'm back for more, (wanna make love to ya baby)
Set your spirit free, it's the only way to be.

Waiting in Vain

Words & Music by Bob Marley

'cause I know how to do my thing.
but your love is my re - lief.
Don't talk to me as
Tears in my eyes burn,

if you think I'm dumb.
tears in my eyes burn while I'm wait - ing,
I wan - na know when you're gon - na come.
while I'm wait - ing for my turn.

See, I don't wan - na wait in vain for your love.

To Coda

I don't wan - na wait in vain for your love.
I don't wan - na wait in

vain for your love. 'Cause it's sum - mer is here,
I'm still wait - ing there.

Win - ter is here and I'm still wait - ing there.

D. S. al Coda

1.
2.

(Guitar solo)

Like I said,

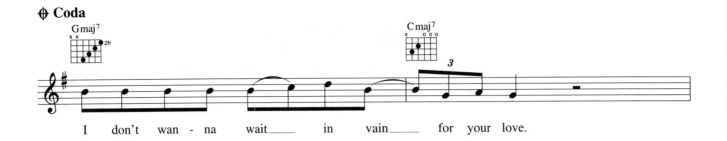

I don't wan - na wait____ in vain____ for your love.

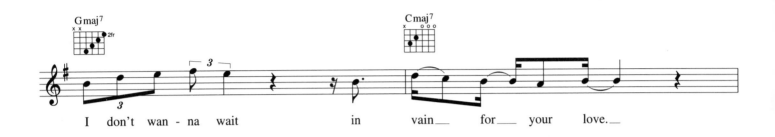

I don't wan - na wait in vain____ for____ your love.____

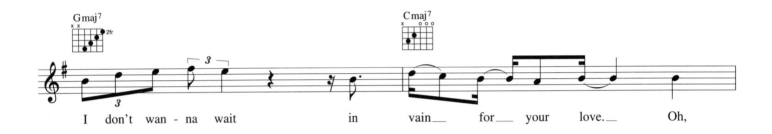

I don't wan - na wait in vain____ for____ your love.____ Oh,

I don't wan - na I don't wan - na, I don't wan - na, I don't wan - na, I don't wan - na wait in vain.__ No,

I don't wan - na, I don't wan - na, I don't wan - na, I don't wan - na, I don't wan - na wait in vain.__ It's your

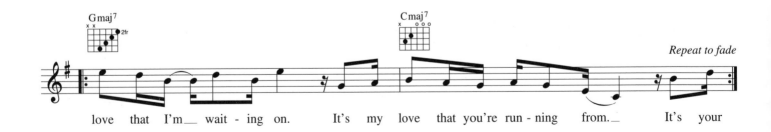

love that I'm__ wait - ing on. It's my love that you're run - ning from.__ It's your

Waterloo

Words & Music by Benny Andersson, Stig Anderson & Bjorn Ulvaeus

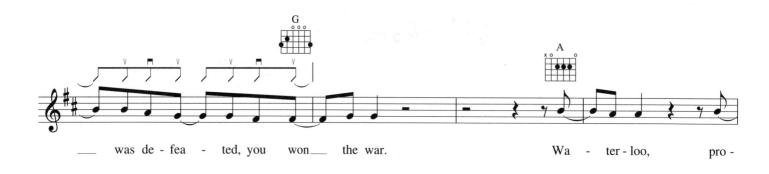

was de - fea - ted, you won the war.   Wa - ter - loo,   pro -

- mise to love you for ev - er more.   Wa - ter - loo,   could -

- n't es - cape if I want - ed to.   Wa - ter - loo,   know -

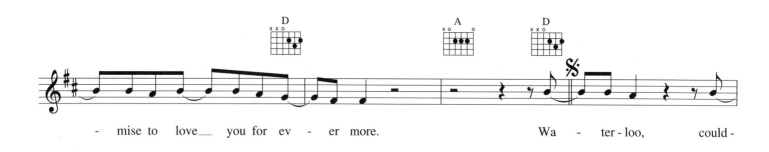

- ing my fate is to be with you.   Wa, Wa Wa Wa Wa - ter - loo,   fi -

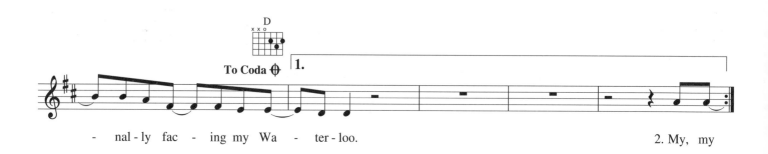

To Coda ✛ **1.**

- nal - ly fac - ing my Wa - ter - loo.   2. My, my

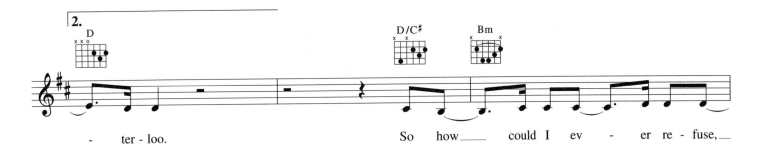

-ter - loo. So how___ could I ev - er re - fuse,___

___ I feel___ like I win___ when I lose.___ Wa -

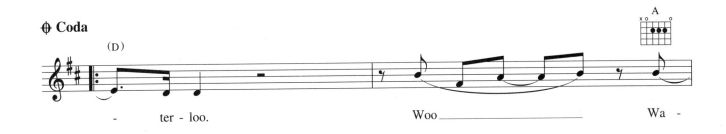

-ter - loo. Woo_____ Wa -

-ter - loo, know - ing my fate___ is to be___ with you. Wa,___

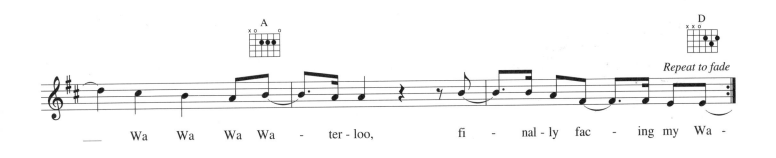

___ Wa Wa Wa Wa - ter - loo, fi - nal - ly fac - ing my Wa -

145

Where Angels Play

Words & Music by Ian Brown & John Squire

Verse

1. "O. K.___ let's fly"___ she says, "This car - pet's made_ for two."_____
2. Out be-low___ the coun - try rolls___ like a migh-ty boil - ing sea._____

This ug - ly lit - tle box,___ no place for me___ and you._____
The warm_ red sun gives up___ and sinks in - to___ the trees._____

Our car - pet falls_____ on a dew - fresh daf-fo - dil plain.___ }
But I'm no fool,_____ I can't stand here betrayed._ }

Take a look a - round,___ there's some - thing hap - pen - ing, all the col - ours fade._

Chorus

_____ I don't want_ you now,_ bang

bang bang gone._ Ooh,___ I don't need_ you now,_ the

147

Wishing Well

Words & Music by Paul Rodgers, Simon Kirke, Tetsu Yamauchi,
John Bundrick & Paul Kossoff

al - ways say - in' fare - well._____ And the on - ly time___ that you're___

some - thing you just can't tell._____

1.

___ sat - is - fied___ is with your feet in the wish - ing well._____

1. cont.

Oh,_____ whoa.___ Dig this…

2.

Oh,_____ whoa._____ yeah, yeah.

Bridge

Strum pattern

But I know___ what you're_ wish - ing for._____

Yeah._____ Oh_____ yeah_____

(Love in a peaceful world.) (Love in a peaceful world.)

Woman

Words & Music by John Lennon

Capo 1st fret to play with original recording

1. Wo - man, I can hard - ly ex - press my raised e - mo - tions at my thought - less - ness,___ af - ter all___ I'm for - ev - er in___ your debt.___ And wo - man I will try to ex - press___ my in - ner feel - ings and thank - ful - ness___ for show ing me the mean - ing of suc - cess.___

2. Wo - man, I know you un - der - stand the lit - tle child in - side the man,___ please re - mem - ber, my life is in___ your hands.___ And wo - man hold me close to your heart___ how - ev - er dis - tant don't keep us a - part,___ af - ter all it is writ - ten in the stars.___

Woodstock

Words & Music by Joni Mitchell

1. I came up-on____ a child____ of God,____ he was
2. can I walk be-side you? I have

walk-ing a-long____ the road and I asked him; "Where are you
come here to lose____ the smog, and I feel to be a

go-ing?"____ And this he told me. "I'm
cog in some-thing turn - ing. Well

goin' on down____ to Yas - gur's farm,____ I'm gon-na join in a rock____ 'n' roll
maybe it is____ just the time of year,____ or may-be it's the time of

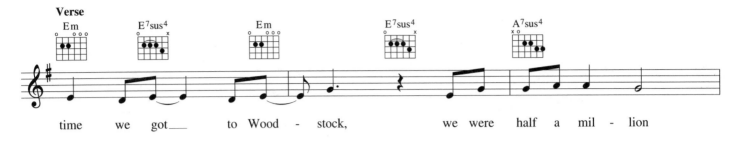

Verse

time we got___ to Wood - stock, we were half a mil - lion

strong, and___ ev - 'ry - where___ there was song and___

ce - le - bra - tion.___ And I dreamed I___ saw the

bomb - ers rid - ing shot - gun in the sky and they were turn - ing

in - to but - ter - flies___ a - bove___ our___ na -

Chorus

- tion.___ We are star - dust,

mil - lion year___ old car - bon, we are gold - en,

caught in the de - vil's bar - gain, and we've got to get___ our -

- selves back to the gar - den.___

Outro
Freely

Ah.___

Ah.___

w/ad lib vocal

Wonderful Tonight

Words & Music by Eric Clapton

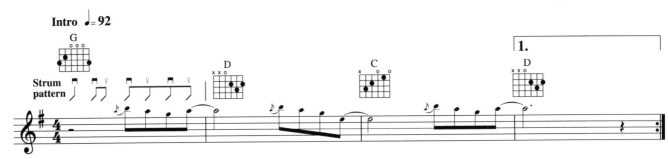

1. It's late in the eve - ning,___ she's won-d'ring what clothes.
2. We go to a par - ty,___ and ev - ery-one turns___
3.(𝄋) It's time to go home___ now,___ and I've got an ach - ing

___ to wear,___ she puts on her make - up,___ and brush-es her long___
___ to see,___ this beau - ti - ful lad - y, is walk-ing a-round___
head,___ so I give her the car___ keys___ and she helps me to

___ blonde hair.___ And then she asks___ me, "Do I look al - right?"
___ with me.___ And then she asks___ me, "Do you feel al - right?"
bed. ___ And then I tell___ her, as I turn out the light___

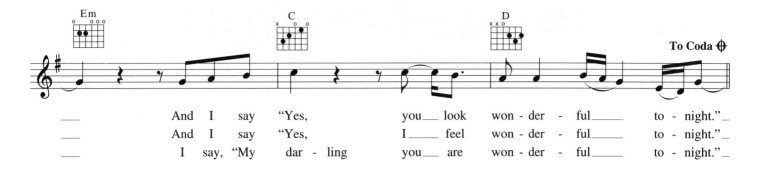

And I say "Yes, you look won-der-ful to-night."
And I say "Yes, I feel won-der-ful to-night."
I say, "My dar-ling you are won-der-ful to-night."

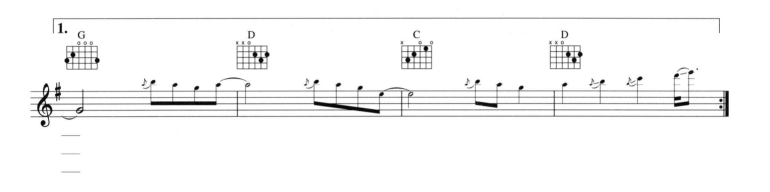

2.

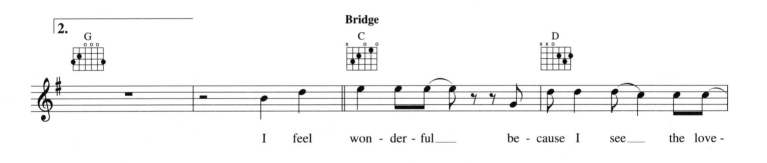

Bridge

I feel won-der-ful be-cause I see the love-

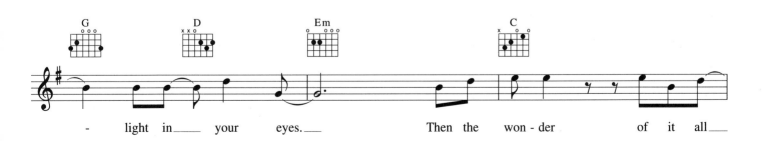

- light in your eyes. Then the won-der of it all

is that you just don't_ re - a - lise_____ how much___ I love___

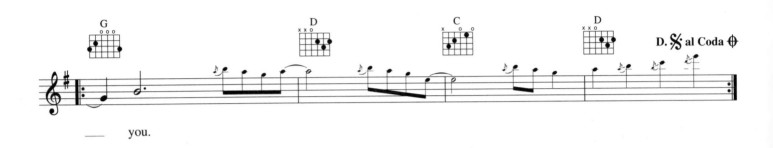

D. 𝄋 al Coda ⨁

___ you.

⨁ Coda

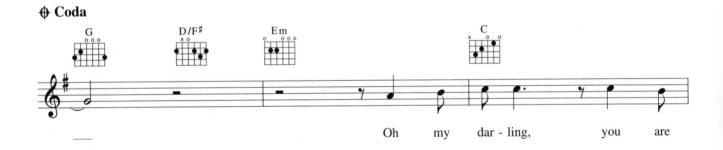

Oh my dar - ling, you are

Outro

won - der - ful_____ to - night._____

rall. 2°

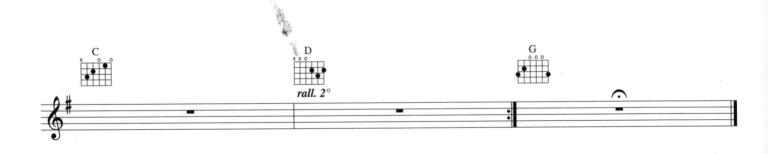